JMP® INTRODUCTORY GUIDE
Version 3 of JMP

"The real voyage of discovery consists not in seeking new
landscapes, but in having new eyes."

Mercel Proust

SAS Institute Inc.
SAS Campus Drive
Cary, NC 27513

JMP® Introductory Guide, Version 3

Contents

Origin

JMP was 100% developed by SAS Institute Inc., Cary NC. The product consists of about 160,000 lines of C code. However, it is not a part of the SAS System and is not as portable as SAS. A SAS add–on product called SAS/INSIGHT is related to JMP in some ways, but has different conventions and capabilities. Portions of JMP were adapted from routines in the SAS System, particularly for linear algebra, and probability calculations. Version 1 of JMP went into production in October, 1989.

Credits

JMP was conceived and started by John Sall. Design and development was done by John Sall, Katherine Ng, Michael Hecht, David Tilley, and Richard Potter. Ann Lehman coordinated product development, production, and documentation. William Gjertsen, ambassador-at-large, interacts continuously with clients to provide current user feedback. Jeffrey Perkinson provides technical support and conducted test site administration. Annie Dudley headed testing for JMP Version 3, with contributions from Kristin Latour and the SAS Institute Quality Assurance department. Sales and sales support include Mary Ann Hansen, Kathryn Wise, and Chris Brown. Additional support is provided by Ruth Lee, Laura Wilson, Miranda Drake, Miriam Leyda, and Kelly Roeder, and past support by Kathy Kiraly and Russell Gardner.

The JMP manuals were written by Ann Lehman and John Sall with contributions and support from Kristin Latour, Mary Cole and Aaron Walker. Editing was done by Patricia Moell. Document production coordination was done by Curt Yeo. Production assistance included Patrice Cherry, Mike Pezzoni, Jennifer Albrecht and Lynn Friebel, graphic arts; Walt Martin, Postscript support; Aaron Walker, and Eric Gjertsen, indexing and help file implementation.

Special thanks to Jim Goodnight for supporting a product outside the usual traditions, and to Dave DeLong, for valuable ideas and advice on statistical and computational matters.

Thanks also to Robert N. Rodriguez and Ying So for statistical editorial support and statistical QC advice. Thanks to Georges Guirguis, Warren Sarle, Randall Tobias, Gordon Johnston, Ying So, Wolfgang Hartmann, Russell Wolfinger, Jane Pierce, and Warren Kuhfeld for statistical R&D support. Additional editorial support was provided by John Hansen, Marsha Russo, Dea Zullo, and Dee Stribling. Additional testing by Jeanne Martin, Fouad Younan, Jeff Schrilla, Jack Berry, Kari Richardson, Jim Borek, Kay Bydalek, Frank Lassiter. Additional technical support is provided by Jenny Kendall, Elizabeth Shaw, Mike Stockstill, and Duane Hayes. Thanks to Steve Shack, Greg Weier, and Maura Stokes for testing Version 1. Also thanks to Eddie Routten, John Boling, David Schlotzhauer, Donna Woodward, and William Fehlner.

Acknowledgments

We owe special gratitude to the people that encouraged us to start JMP, to the alpha and beta testers of JMP, and to the reviewers of the documentation. In particular we thank Al Best, Robert Muenchen, Stan Young, Lenore Hertzenberg, Morgan Wise, Frederick Dalleska, Stuart Janis, Larry Sue, Ramon Leon, Tom Lange, Homer Hegedus, Skip Weed, Michael Emptage, Mathew Lay, Tim Rey, Rubin Gabriel, Michael Friendly, Joe

Hockmen, Frank Shen, J.H. Goodman, Brian Ruff, and David Ikle. Also, we thank Charles Shipp, Harold Gugel, William Lisowski, David Morganstein, Tom Esposito, Susan West, Jim Winters, Chris Fehily, James Mulherin, Dan Chilko, Jim Shook, Bud Martin, George Fraction, Al Fulmer, Cary Tuckfield, Hal Queen, Linda Blazek, Ron Thisted, Ken Bodner, Donna Fulenwider, Nancy McDermott, Rick Blahunka, and Dana C. Aultman.

We also thank the following individuals for expert advice in their statistical specialties: R. Hocking and P. Spector for advice on effective hypotheses; Jason Hsu for advice on multiple comparisons methods (not all of which we were able to incorporate in JMP); Ralph O'Brien for advice on homogeneity of variance tests; Ralph O'Brien and S. Paul Wright for advice on statistical power; Keith Muller for advice in multivariate methods, Dave Trindade for advice on Weibull plots; Lijian Yang and J..S. Marron for bivariate smoothing design.

For sample data, thanks to Patrice Strahle for Pareto examples, the Texas air control board for the pollution data, and David Coleman for the pollen (eureka) data.

Technology License Notices

JMP software contains portions of the file translation library of MacLinkPlus, a product of DataViz Inc., 55 Corporate Drive, Trumbull, CT 06611, (203) 268-0030

Chapter 1
Introducing JMP

We are happy to share JMP with you. This product lets you use an extraordinary graphical interface to display and analyze data. JMP is software for interactive statistical graphics and includes

- a spreadsheet for viewing, editing, entering, and manipulating data
- a broad range of graphical and statistical methods for data analysis
- options to highlight and display subsets of the data
- data management tools for sorting and combining tables
- a calculator for each table column to compute values
- a facility for grouping data and computing summary statistics
- special plots, charts and communication capability for quality improvement techniques
- tools for moving analysis results between applications and for printing
- a scripting language for saving frequently used routines.

JMP is easy to learn. You can begin immediately and see graphical and statistical results quickly by applying the techniques presented in this book. This introductory chapter gives you some basic information about using JMP and takes you on a guided tour.

Preliminaries

Learning about JMP

On Your Own
with JMP Help

If you are familiar with Macintosh or Microsoft Windows software, you may want to proceed on your own. After you install JMP, you can open any of the JMP files in the SAMPLE DATA folder and experiment with analysis tools. Help is available for most menus, options, and reports.

There are several ways to see JMP Help:

- Select **About JMP** from the Apple menu on the Macintosh or **Contents** command from the **Help** menu of Microsoft Windows. This displays the About JMP window with a list of help buttons. Your cursor becomes a question mark as it passes over the buttons. When you click a button, JMP leads you through help about that topic.
- Click the **Statistical Guide** button on the About JMP screen. The JMP Statistical Guide is a scrolling alphabetical reference that tells you how to generate specific analyses using JMP and gives you a button that accesses further help for that topic. The **About JMP** command in the **Help** menu under Windows displays the JMP Statistical Guide
- You can also choose **Help** from dialogs and from pop–up menus in JMP report windows.
- After you generate a report contact sensitive help is available. Select the help tool (**?**) from the **Tools** menu and click the report surface. Context–sensitive help tells about the items in the report window.
- If you are using Microsoft Windows, other typical Help commands are available under the **Help** menu on the main menu bar.
- If you use a Macintosh with Version 7 system software, balloon help is available..

Reading
about JMP

The *JMP User's Guide* has complete documentation of all JMP menus, an explanation of data table manipulation, and a description of the calculator. There are chapters that show you how to do common tasks such as manipulating files, transforming data table columns, and cutting and pasting JMP data, statistical text reports, and graphical displays.

The *JMP Statistics and Graphics Guide* documents statistical platforms, discusses statistical methods, and describes all report windows and options.

Completing Tutorials This introductory book is a collection of tutorials designed to help you learn JMP strategies. The JMP tutorials range from single–step procedures to complex analyses. You can read the tutorials for reference, or work through them step by step. Each tutorial uses a file from the sample data folder. By following these examples, you can quickly become familiar with JMP menus, graphical displays, options, and report windows.

Conventions used in this manual were devised to help you relate written material to information you see on your screen.

• Reference to unopened JMP file names on the Macintosh appear capitalized (ANIMALS). Under Windows unopened JMP files are referred to in lower case letters (animals.jmp), which is the way they appear in a Windows open file list. Most open JMP data table names used in examples are capitalized (ANIMALS or ANIMALS.JMP).

• Note→ Special information, warnings, and limitations are noted as such with an arrow as shown in this note.

• Reference to menu names (**File** menu) or menu items (**Save** command) appear in **Helvetica bold** font, similar to the way they look on your screen.

• References to variable names in data tables and items in reports show in either Helvetica or **Helvetica bold**, according to the way they appear in the book illustration.

• Words or phrases that are important or have definitions specific to JMP are in italics the first time you see them.

Note→ Because the form of JMP file names and open JMP table names is different between the Macintosh an Microsoft Windows, reference to tables will usually use the Macintosh name followed by the Windows name in parentheses.

What You Need to Know...

About using your Machine Before you begin using JMP, you should be familiar with standard operations and terminology such as *click*, *double–click*, *COMMAND–click* and *OPTION–click* on the Macintosh (*CONTROL–click* and *ALT–click* under Windows), *SHIFT–click*, *drag*, *select*, *copy*, and *paste*. You should also know how to use menu bars and scroll bars, how to move and resize windows, and how to manipulate files in the desktop. If you are using your Macintosh or Microsoft Windows for the first time, consult the reference guides that came with the system for more information.

About Statistics   You can use JMP with a minimal background in formal statistical training. All analysis platforms include graphical displays with options that help you review and interpret the results. Each platform also includes access to help windows that offer general help and some statistical details. There are also tutorials in this book that provide examples of displaying and analyzing data.

JMP Basics

To use JMP, you need to know how to start a JMP session, create a data table and use a JMP spreadsheet, select an analysis platform, and end a JMP session. The following sections give you a quick lesson in JMP Basics.

Starting a JMP Session

Start a JMP session by double–clicking the JMP application icon. When JMP is active, you see the following menu bar:

Figure 1.1 The Menu Bar

Macintosh

⚫ File Edit Tables Rows Cols Analyze Graph Tools Window

Windows

File Edit Tables Rows Cols Analyze Graph Tools Window Help

You also see the untitled JMP data table shown in **Figure 1.2**. The new spreadsheet is available for you to key in your own data but is not needed for this tutorial. To close the data table, click the close box in the upper left corner of the window.

Figure 1.2 A New Untitled JMP Spreadsheet

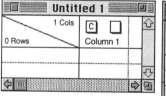 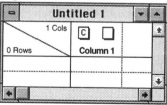

Creating a JMP Data Table

Before you can use JMP commands, you need access to data in an open JMP table. There are three ways to do this:

- The **New** command creates an empty data table in spreadsheet form. You add rows and columns, and then type in or paste in new data.
- The **Import** command creates a JMP table using data exported from other applications.
- The **Open** command gives you the standard file selection dialog with a list of existing JMP tables you can open. The sample data folder that comes with your JMP package is a collection of JMP tables.

To continue with this demonstration, select **Open** from the **File** menu.

Figure 1.3 The **Open** Command in the **File** Menu

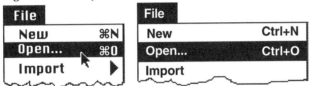

When the **Open** file dialog appears, select and open the file called TYPING DATA (typing.jmp under Windows).

Using the Spreadsheet

Opening a file on your disk creates a data table in memory that appears in spreadsheet form with rows and columns as shown in **Figure 1.4**. The counts of rows and columns appear in the upper left corner of the spreadsheet. A row number identifies each row, and each column has a column name. Rows and columns are sometimes called observations and variables in an analysis.

Figure 1.4 The TYPING DATA Spreadsheet

TYPING.JMP		
2 Cols	N ☐	C ☐
17 Rows	**brand**	**speed**
1	REGAL	70
2	SPEEDYTYPE	87
3	SPEEDYTYPE	79
4	REGAL	73
5	SPEEDYTYPE	77
6	REGAL	72

The JMP data table is a flexible spreadsheet for preparing data. Using it, you can do a variety of data table management tasks including

- editing the value in any cell
- changing a column's width by dragging the column line
- hiding columns temporarily or deleting columns permanently
- rearranging the order of columns
- selecting a subset of rows for analysis
- sorting a table
- combining tables.

Cursor Forms

To navigate in the spreadsheet, you need to understand how the cursor works in each part of the spreadsheet. The cursor assumes different forms and has different functions depending on its location in the spreadsheet. These forms and functions are described below.

Arrow Cursor

The cursor displays as a standard arrow when it is in the *modeling type box* or the *role assignment box* as shown in **Figure 1.5**. It is also a standard arrow when it is in the *Cols* or *Rows* triangular areas in the upper left corner of the spreadsheet.

Figure 1.5 Arrow Cursor in the Spreadsheet

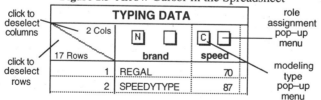

Cross Cursor When the cursor is within the heading of a selected column or a data cell in an active spreadsheet, it becomes a large cross. This means it is available to select text. When you click the cross cursor, the text highlights and can be edited. The cursor then becomes an I–beam.

Figure 1.6 Cross Cursor in the Spreadsheet

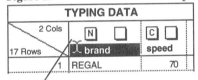

cross cursor:
click to select text for editing

I–beam Cursor To edit text, position the I–beam within highlighted characters. Click next to any character to mark an insertion point. The I–beam deposits a vertical blinking bar. Alternatively, drag the I–beam to select a portion of the text for replacement. By default, the entire character string is selected. Use the keyboard to make changes after positioning the I–beam. To edit a column name, as shown in **Figure 1.7**, first click the column selection area to highlight the column (see **Figure 1.8**). Click a second time to highlight the column name for editing.

Figure 1.7 I–beam Cursor in the Spreadsheet

I-beam:
click or drag to edit text

Open Cross Cursor The cursor becomes a large open cross when you move it into a column or row selection area. Use the open cross cursor to select a single row or column. Shift–click a beginning and ending row or a beginning and ending column to select an entire array. Use COMMAND–click on the Macintosh and CONTROL–click under Windows to select multiple rows or columns that are not contiguous. See the next section for a more detailed explanation of selecting rows and columns.

Figure 1.8 Large Cross Cursor in the Spreadsheet

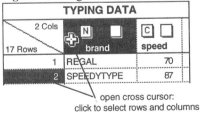

open cross cursor:
click to select rows and columns

Double Arrow Cursor — The cursor changes to a double–arrow cursor when you position it on a column boundary. Dragging the double–arrow cursor changes the column width.

Figure 1.9 Double Arrow Cursor in the Spreadsheet

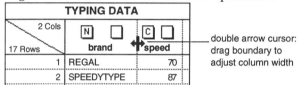

Selecting Rows and Columns

You select rows and columns in a JMP spreadsheet by highlighting them as shown in **Figure 1.10**. To highlight a row, click the space that contains the row number. To highlight a column, click the background area above the column name.

To extend a selection of rows or columns, drag the cursor across the array or SHIFT–click the first and last rows or columns of the desired range. To make a discontiguous selection, use COMMAND–click on the Macintosh (CONTROL–click under Windows)on the desired selections.

Figure 1.10 Select Rows and Columns

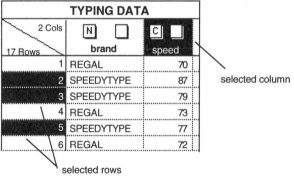

COMMAND–click (or CONTROL–click under Windows) on a row or column to deselect it. To deselect all rows or columns, click the appropriate triangular area in the upper left corner of the spreadsheet.

Specifying the Data Column Modeling Type

The small box just above the column name is a pop–up menu used to declare the modeling type of the values in the column.

Figure 1.11 Modeling Type Pop–up Menu

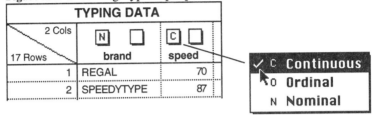

JMP uses three modeling types:

- **Continuous** values are numeric measurements.
- **Ordinal** values are ordered numeric or character values.
- **Nominal** values are numeric or character classifications.

The default modeling type is nominal for character values and continuous for numeric values. In **Figure 1.11**, the column called brand is a nominal variable and speed is a continuous variable.

You can assign each column a modeling type appropriate for the next analysis by using its modeling type pop–up menu (see **Figure 1.11**). JMP uses the modeling type to determine how to analyze the column's values.

Choosing Variable Roles

The JMP analysis methods are like stages or platforms for variables to dramatize their values. Each analysis platform requires information about what role the variables are to play in analysis. You can specify variable roles by

- using the role assignment box at the top of each column in the spreadsheet
- selecting a command from the **Analyze** or **Graph** menus and responding to a specific assign–roles prompt
- using the **Assign Roles** command from the **Cols** menu.

Role assignment boxes in the spreadsheet are pop–up menus. Drag to the appropriate selection for your analysis as shown in **Figure 1.12**. You can change a variable's role at any time or drop it from analysis by selecting **None** from the role assignment pop–up menu.

Figure 1.12 The Role Assignment Pop–Up Menu

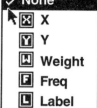

The following list describes each role:

- **None** means the column is not included in the analysis.
- **X** identifies a column as an independent, classification, or explanatory variable whose values divide the rows into sample groups.
- **Y** identifies a column as a response or dependent variable whose distribution is to be studied.
- **Weight** identifies a column whose values supply weights for each response.
- **Freq** identifies a column whose values assign a frequency to each row for the analysis.
- **Label** identifies a column whose values specify a labeling convention for points in plots.

When you choose a variable's role using the role selection menu or the **Assign Roles** command, the role appears in the role selection box as shown in **Figure 1.13**. Roles remain in effect until you change them.

Continue with this demonstration by identifying both the brand and speed columns as Y variables in the TYPING DATA spreadsheet.

Figure 1.13 Choose Variable Roles

Selecting an Analysis Platform

There are a variety of analysis and display platforms available in JMP through commands in the **Analyze** and **Graph** menus. Each command produces a graphical display and optional statistical text reports. For example, to see histograms of all Y columns in the active spreadsheet, select the **Distribution of Y** command from the **Analyze** menu.

Figure 1.14 Select an Analysis Platform

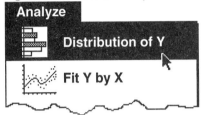

Graphical Display of Data

The **Distribution of Y** analysis creates a report window containing a graphical display of all Y columns in the TYPING DATA (typing.jmp) table. For this example, the **Distribution of Y** command produces the graphical displays shown in **Figure 1.15**, which include

- histograms of both the brand and speed columns
- a mosaic (stacked bar) chart of the nominal variable, **brand**
- an outlier box plot of the continuous variable, **speed**.

Figure 1.15 Distribution of Y Graphical Displays

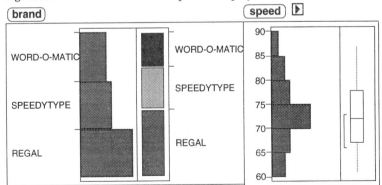

Adjust the histogram bars

To adjust the histogram bars, select the hand tool from the **Tools** menu. Use the hand to *grab* the chart you want to change. Moving the hand to the left combines intervals and shows fewer bars. Moving the hand to the right produces a finer division of each interval and shows more bars. Moving the hand up or down maintains the number of bars but changes the boundary of the bars on the axis and redistributes the data.

Figure 1.16 Adjust the Number of Bars

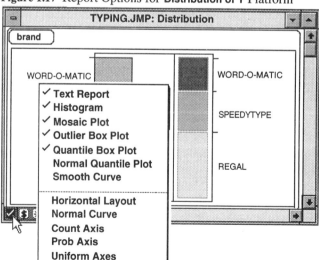

Note➡ Click anywhere in the plot to see a small resize box in the lower right corner. Click and drag the resize box to change the plot size.

Display options

The plots are one of several optional representations of data. The check mark (✓) at the left corner of the horizontal scroll bar accesses a pop–up menu that lists available report options. For practice, try selecting different combinations of these options and watch the effect they have on the displays and reports.

Figure 1.17 Report Options for **Distribution of Y** Platform

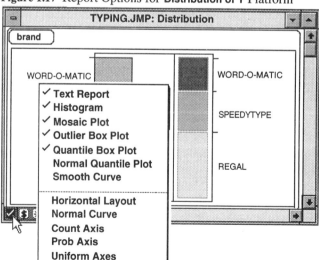

Statistical Reports

When the **Text Report** option is checked, *reveal/conceal* text report buttons accompany each graph. You can click these buttons to show or hide statistical text reports. The kinds of tables depend on whether a variable is continuous, ordinal, or nominal.

For an continuous variable, JMP displays a Quantiles and a Moments table. **Figure 1.18** shows these reports for the speed variable from the TYPING DATA (typing.jmp) table.

Note➡ The **Horizontal Layout** option found in the check (✓) pop–up menu produces the layout of the text report shown in **Figure 1.18**.

Figure 1.18 Reports for Continuous Variables

Quantiles		
maximum	100.0%	87.000
	99.5%	87.000
	97.5%	87.000
	90.0%	82.200
quartile	75.0%	78.000
median	50.0%	72.000
quartile	25.0%	67.000
	10.0%	61.800
	2.5%	61.000
	0.5%	61.000
minimum	0.0%	61.000

Moments	
Mean	72.47059
Std Dev	7.00105
Std Err Mean	1.69800
upper 95% Mean	76.07018
lower 95% Mean	68.87100
N	17.00000
Sum Wgts	17.00000

For nominal and ordinal variables, the Frequency table shows the total sample frequency, category frequencies, and associated probabilities. **Figure 1.19** shows the table for the variable brand from the TYPING DATA (typing.jmp) table.

Figure 1.19 Frequency Table for Nominal or Ordinal Variables

Level	Count	Probability	Cum Prob
REGAL	8	0.47059	0.47059
SPEEDYTYPE	5	0.29412	0.76471
WORD-O-MATIC	4	0.23529	1.00000
Total	17		

Completing a JMP Session

After you complete an analysis, you can use JMP tools to copy any part of a report window into the clipboard. If you want, you can close the report window or the spreadsheet without quitting JMP.

- To close a report window, click the close box in the upper left corner of the window.
- To close a spreadsheet, either click the close box in the upper left corner of the spreadsheet or choose **Close** from the **File** menu while the spreadsheet is the active window. If you have made changes to the spreadsheet, a dialog asks if you want to save or discard the changes to the data table. The dialog also asks if you want to close related windows (if any are still open).

To end a JMP session, select **Quit** from the **File** Menu.

Take A Quick Spin

The following example takes you on a short guided tour through a JMP session. Follow the steps to see a three–dimensional spinning plot.

Open a Data Table

1. Open the file called COWBOY HAT (cowboy.jmp in the data folder under Windows)to begin a JMP session. The spreadsheet shown in **Figure 1.20** appears.

Figure 1.20 The COWBOY HAT Spreadsheet

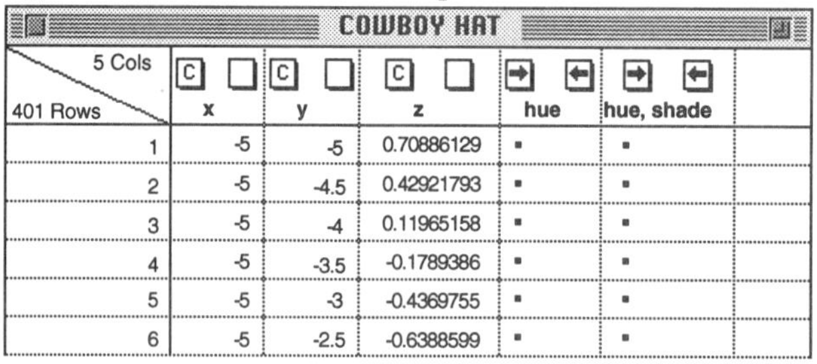

COWBOY HAT					
5 Cols	C ☐	C ☐	C ☐	➡ ⬅	➡ ⬅
401 Rows	x	y	z	hue	hue, shade
1	-5	-5	0.70886129	▪	▪
2	-5	-4.5	0.42921793	▪	▪
3	-5	-4	0.11965158	▪	▪
4	-5	-3.5	-0.1789386	▪	▪
5	-5	-3	-0.4369755	▪	▪
6	-5	-2.5	-0.6388599	▪	▪

This spreadsheet has three numeric columns and two *row state* columns. Columns **x** and **y** are x and y coordinates, and **z** was created using the function

$$z = \text{sine} \sqrt{x^2 + y^2}$$

The columns called **hue** and **hue, shade** contain special row state information used to plot points.

2 The pop–up menu at the top of a row state column differs from those above numerical and character data columns. Use the Row State pop–up menu at the top of the **hue** column to activate its row state information. The active row state information appears to the left of the row numbers as shown in **Figure 1.21.**

Figure 1.21 Active Row States

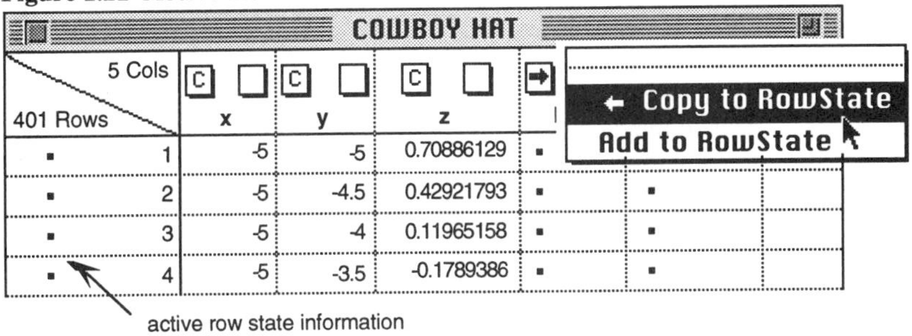

COWBOY HAT
5 Cols
401 Rows
x
y
z
Copy to RowState
Add to RowState
1 -5 -5 0.70886129
2 -5 -4.5 0.42921793
3 -5 -4 0.11965158
4 -5 -3.5 -0.1789386
active row state information

Select an Analysis Platform

3 To plot the three columns of information from the COWBOY HAT (COWBOY.JMP) data table, choose the **Spinning Plot** platform from the **Graph** menu.

Figure 1.22 The **Spinning Plot** Command on the **Graph** Menu

Graph
Bar/Pie Charts
Overlay Plots
Spinning Plot

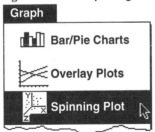

4 When you release the mouse button, the dialog shown in **Figure 1.23** prompts you to select columns for the Spinning Plot platform. Select the **x**, **y**, and **z** columns from the column selector list on the left side of the dialog, and click the **Add** button. These column names now appear in the column on the right side of the dialog. On the Macintosh you can also select columns to analyze by clicking on them in the columns box and dragging them over to the upper right box.

Figure 1.23 The Spinning Plot Column Selection Dialog

SPINNING PLOT
Select X and Y Columns.

Columns from COWBOY HAT

X	> Add >	X
Y		Y
Z	Remove	
	> Wt >	
	> Freq >	
	> Lbl >	

Help   Cancel   OK

5   When you click **Done**, the Spinning Plot platform appears. The points in the COWBOY HAT (COWBOY.JMP) data table initially show as a contour plot because the **z** dimension is projected onto the **x**, **y** plane.

Spin the Cowboy Hat

6   Next, using the **Tools** menu, change the standard arrow cursor to the hand tool. Position the hand tool on the cowboy hat spinning plot, hold down the mouse button, and move the hand about. The cowboy hat moves in three dimensions as shown in **Figure 1.24**.

The plot can also spin by itself. Hold down the shift key, and give the plot a push with the hand tool.

To stop the spinning plot, click in any JMP window.

Figure 1.24 The Cowboy Hat in Three Dimensions

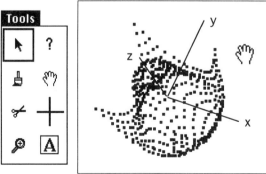

Precision Spinning

The spin control panel, shown in **Figure 1.25**, contains twelve small icons. These icons control the spinning plot.

The six directional arrows are buttons that control the spin of the three–dimensional image. If you click one of these arrows, the plot spins in the direction indicated. The spin continues as long as you hold down the mouse button. However, you can shift–click a directional arrow to make the plot spin continuously. Clicking anywhere in the display stops the spin. The other six icons control spin rate, plot scale, and various display options:

- Clicking either the + or – angle icon increases or decreases the rate of the next spin, respectively.
- The two four–way arrows adjust the scale of the plot as indicated by their arrows.
- The triangle icon accesses the pop–up menu of display options shown in the next section.
- The home icon resets the spin axes to their original position.

Figure 1.25 Precision Spinning

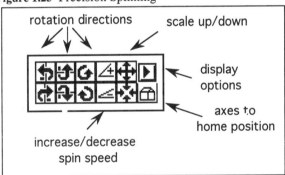

Display Options

The display options, shown in **Figure 1.26**, let you tailor the spinning plot. By default, the background is black and the axes are visible. You can change these conditions by selecting different options from this pop–up menu. Each option switches on and off alternately when you select it.

Complete your experiment with the spinning cowboy hat by trying out a few of the display options.

Figure 1.26 Display Options

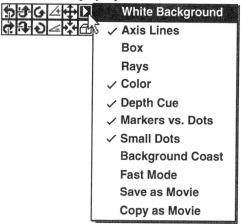

When you finish,

- close the Spinning Plot platform by clicking the close box in the upper left corner of the window.
- close the COWBOY HAT (COWBOY.JMP) spreadsheet by clicking its close box.

To close the JMP application, choose **Quit** from the **File** menu.

Chapter 2
Creating a JMP Data Table

A researcher wants to evaluate a new drug developed to lower blood pressure. Data were recorded a over six months period for the following treatment groups:

- drug, 300 mg
- drug, 450 mg
- placebo
- control.

The researcher has the mean monthly blood pressure for each group recorded in a journal and wants to plot them. A lab assistant has the task of using JMP to enter data values into the computer and to create a single neat and informative line chart that shows the study results.

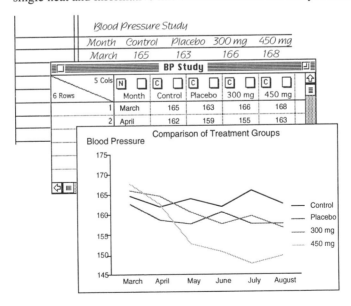

Starting a JMP Session

1 The lab assistant double–clicks the JMP application icon to begin a JMP session. The active JMP application displays the main menu bar, shown in **Figure 2.1**.

Figure 2.1 The Menu Bar

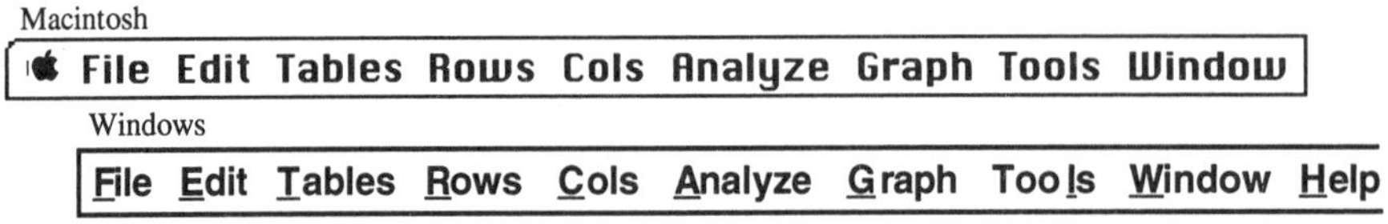

Macintosh
File Edit Tables Rows Cols Analyze Graph Tools Window
Windows
File Edit Tables Rows Cols Analyze Graph Tools Window Help

The untitled JMP spreadsheet shown in **Figure 2.2** automatically opens for entering data. The **New** command in the **File** menu also creates a new untitled data table.

Figure 2.2 A New Untitled JMP Spreadsheet

Untitled 1
1 Cols
0 Rows
Column 1
Untitled 1
1 Cols
0 Rows
Column 1

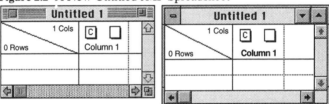

The data values are blood pressure statistics collected over six months and recorded in a notebook page as shown in **Figure 2.3**. The lab assistant can quickly key this raw data into a JMP data table.

Figure 2.3 Notebook of Raw Study Data

Blood Pressure Study

Month	Control	Placebo	300 mg	450 mg
March	165	163	166	168
April	162	159	165	163
May	164	158	161	153
June	162	161	158	151
July	166	158	160	148
August	163	158	157	150

Creating Rows and Columns in a JMP Data Table

JMP data tables have rows and columns, sometimes called observations and variables in statistical terms. The raw data in **Figure 2.3** are arranged as five columns (treatment groups) and six rows (months March through August). The first line in the notebook names each column of values, which can be used as column names in a JMP table.

Add Columns

2 One way to begin entering data is to first create the number of rows and columns you want. The lab assistant selects the **Add Columns** command in the **Cols** menu. The Add Columns dialog (**Figure 2.4**) prompts for the number of columns to add, where to add them, and what type of columns to add. The lab assistant asks for five new columns.

Figure 2.4 The Add Columns Dialog

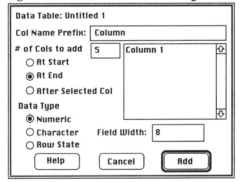

3 The default column names are Column 1, Column 2 but can be changed in the Add Columns dialog. The column names in the table are editable fields so the next step is to type in meaningful names. The lab assistant uses the names from the data journal—Month, Control, Placebo, 300 mg, and 450 mg.

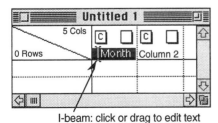

I-beam: click or drag to edit text

To edit a column name, first click the column selection area to highlight the column. Then click a second time and position the I–beam within highlighted characters. Click to mark an insertion point for typing, as shown to the left. The I–beam deposits a vertical blinking bar. Alternatively, drag the I–beam to select a portion of the text for replacement.

Set Column Characteristics

4 Columns can have different characteristics. By default, they contain numeric data, but month names are character values. The lab assistant highlights the Month column by clicking the area above the column name (**Figure 2.5**), and selects the **Column Info** command from the **Cols** menu. This accesses the Column Info dialog shown in **Figure 2.6**.

Figure 2.5 The Column Info Command

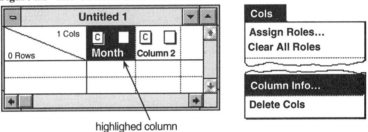

highlighed column

You use the **Data Type** pop–up menu to change Month to a character variable as shown in **Figure 2.6**. You can also use the Column Info dialog to change the other column characteristics, and to access the JMP calculator for computing column values.

Figure 2.6 The Column Info Dialog

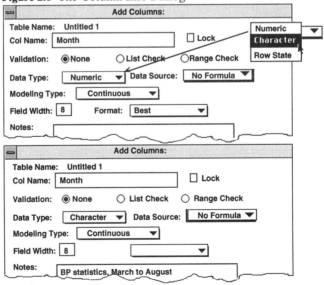

Add Rows

5   Adding rows is also easy. The lab assistant chooses **Add Rows** from the
Rows menu and asks for six new rows as shown in **Figure 2.7**.
Alternatively, if you double–click anywhere in the body of the table, it
automatically fills with new rows up through the position of the cursor.

6   Finally, the lab assistant uses the **Save As** command in the **File** menu to
name the table (**BP Study** or **BPSTUDY.JMP**) and give it a disk a location.

Figure 2.7 The Add Rows Dialog

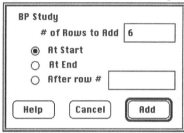

The data table is now ready to hold data values. **Figure 2.8** summarizes
the table evolution so far. The lab assistant began with a new untitled
table and added enough rows and columns to accommodate the raw
data, tailored the characteristics of the table by giving the table and
columns descriptive names, and changed the data type of the Month
column to accept character values.

Figure 2.8 JMP Data Table with New Rows, Columns, and Names

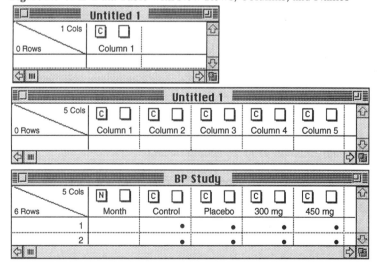

Entering Data

Entering data into the data table is as simple as typing values into their appropriate table cells. The lab assistant types the values from the study journal (**Figure 2.3**) into the **BP STUDY** (**BPSTUDY**.JMP) table as shown in **Figure 2.9**. To enter data into the data table, do the following:

- Move the cursor into a data cell and click to highlight the cell. The cursor shows as an I–beam in the highlighted area.
- Click to see the I–beam deposit a vertical blinking bar.
- Key in numbers or characters.
- To correct a mistake, drag the I-beam across the incorrect entry to highlight it and type the correction over it.

Figure 2.9 Data Entry in a JMP Data Table

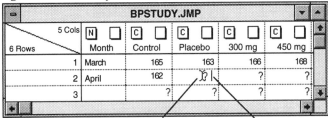

I-Beam   vertical blinking bar

Although you can click any specific cell to edit it, the tab and return keys are useful keyboard tools for data entry.

- Tab moves the cursor one cell to the right. Shift–tab moves the cursor one cell to the left. Moving the cursor with the tab key automatically wraps it to the beginning of the next (or previous) row. Tabbing past the last table cell creates a new row.
- Return moves the cursor down one cell. Shift–return moves the cursor one cell up.

Figure 2.10 Finished Blood Pressure Study Table

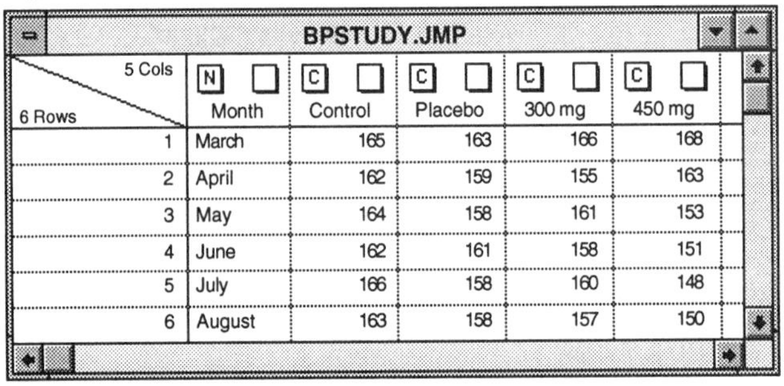

BPSTUDY.JMP				
5 Cols N	C	C	C	C
6 Rows	Month	Control	Placebo	300 mg	450 mg
1	March	165	163	166	168
2	April	162	159	155	163
3	May	164	158	161	153
4	June	162	161	158	151
5	July	166	158	160	148
6	August	163	158	157	150

Plotting Data

Commands in the main menus act only upon JMP data tables. You can use the **Analyze** and **Graph** menu commands to plot information in the **BP Study (BPSTUDY.JMP)** table. To wrap up this project, the lab assistant experiments with the **Overlay Plots** command in the **Graph** menu.

8   The **Analyze** menu commands have to know which columns to work with and what to do with them. The lab assistant wants to plot the months across the horizontal (X) axis and the columns of blood pressure statistics for each treatment group overlaid on the vertical (Y) axis. These X and Y roles can be assigned with the role assignment pop–up menu at the top of each column as shown in **Figure 2.11**.

Figure 2.11 Variable Roles for Plots and Charts

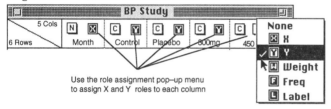
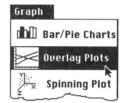

The **Overlay Plot** command in the **Graph** menu displays a message saying it expects a numeric variable for X (Month is character). When you click **OK**, the **Overlay Plot** command automatically accesses the Bar/Pie Charts platform, which is the best way to display a line chart.

By default, Y–axis scaling begins at zero, and the overlay chart looks like the one in **Figure 2.12**. To present easy–to–read information, the Y axis need to be rescaled and the chart needs labels.

Figure 2.12 Default Line Chart

Double–click in Y Axis area for rescale dialog

or use the magnifier tool in the Tools Menu

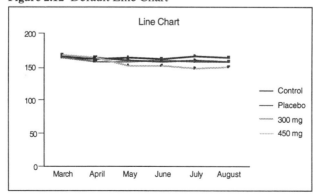

To rescale an axis, double–click anywhere in the axis area and use the rescale dialog shown in **Figure 2.13**.

The rescale dialog lets you

- set the minimum and maximum of the axis scale
- specify the tick marks increment
- request minor tick marks
- request grid lines at major or minor tick marks
- format numeric axes
- use either a linear or log–based scale.
- draw as many reference lines as you want.

Figure 2.13 Axis Rescale Dialog

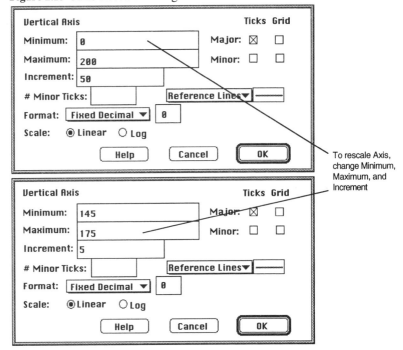

To rescale Axis, change Minimum, Maximum, and Increment

In this example the plotted values range from about 145 to 175. The lab assistant keys these figures into the Axis Rescale dialog for minimum and maximum. Also, the increment for the tick marks need to change from 50 to any number less than the range given by the maximum and . (Peek ahead at **Figure 2.15** to see the dramatic result of axis rescaling.) The chart also needs a title and other documentation to make it easily interpretable. The star (∗) pop–up menu (**Figure 2.14**) located at the

The chart also needs a title and other documentation to make it easily interpretable. The star (*) pop–up menu (**Figure 2.14**) located at the lower left of the window lists options for tailoring the appearance of plots, charts, and other JMP results.

Each time you select the **Title** or **Footnote** options, a new editable text area appears in the title or footnote area of the plot. You can format each title or footnote individually with the **Alignment** and **Font Type** submenus.

Figure 2.14 Star Pop–up Menu for Titles and Footnotes

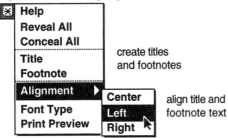

To give the chart a polished appearance, the lab assistant creates a title to label the graph, a second title to label the Y axis, a footnote to label the X axis, and a second footnote for reference.

Titles and footnotes are editable areas at the top and bottom of plots and charts. You can have as many titles and footnotes as you need. Titles can have multiple lines aligned to the left, right, or center of the chart. If you click in the editable area, the area highlights for text entry. If you click the edge of the text area, a small resize box appears at the lower right corner. Dragging this box resizes the editable area.

You can follow these steps with the lab assistant and see the final result shown in **Figure 2.15**:

10

- The title area displays the word "Line Chart" by default. Click to highlight it and type the words "Comparison of Treatment Groups" as the graph title.
- Select **Title** from the star pop–up menu to create a second title area.
- Click the second title area to highlight it and type "Blood Pressure."
- Select **Alignment** from the star pop–up menu and **Left** from its submenu to label the Y axis.
- Select **Footnote** from the star pop–up menu to create a footnote area. Footnotes are left–aligned by default.
- Click the footnote area to highlight it, and type the word "Month."

- Select **Alignment** from the star pop–up menu and **Center** from its submenu to label the X axis.
- Select **Footnote** from the Star pop–up menu to create a second footnote area.

17
- Click the second footnote area to highlight it, and type the word "XYZ Blood Pressure Study, 1993" as footnote documentation for the data source.

Figure 2.15 Line Chart with Modified Y Axis, Titles, and Footnotes

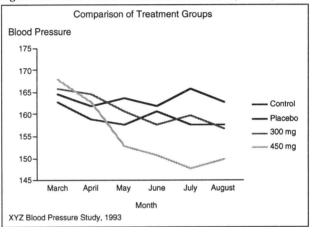

Chapter Summary

A study was done to evaluate the effect of a new drug on blood pressure. A lab assistant is responsible for entering the results into a JMP table and creating plots. To do this the lab assistant

- uses the **New** command in the **File** menu to create a new JMP table
- creates the appropriate number of rows and columns for the data
- types the data into the empty spreadsheet
- assigns X and Y roles and uses the **Overlay Plot** command in the **Graph** menu for plotting, which gives a line chart
- tailors the line chart with axis labels, titles, and footnotes.

Chapter 3
Summarizing Data

The hotdog was dropped from a cafeteria menu because of its reputation as an unhealthy food, possibly classified in the junk food category. Many cafeteria customers feel this is unpatriotic and are upset.

The cafeteria nutritionist wants to resurrect the hotdog as a menu item, but not before looking into the multitude of brands available. The nutritionist has gathered survey information about cost, nutritional ingredients of concern, and taste preference for 54 hotdog brands. This information is sufficient to provide a summary of hotdog statistics and to identify the brands that are

- most nutritious
- least costly
- best tasting.

The taste, cost, and nutritional hotdog variables used in this chapter are an enhancement of data from Moore, D. S., and McCabe G. P., (1989), *Introduction to the Practice of Statistics*, and Consumer Reports (1986). The brand names were changed to fictional names, and the taste preference labels correspond to a taste preference scale.

Look Before You Leap

1 The nutritionist double–clicks on the HOTDOGS file in the SAMPLE DATA folder (called hotdogs.jmp in the data folder under Windows) to start a JMP session and see a spreadsheet view (table) of the file. **Figure 3.1** is a partial listing of the HOTDOGS (or HOTDOGS.JMP) table.

Figure 3.1 The HOTDOGS Data Table

	Product Name	Type	Taste	$/oz	$/lb Protein	Calories	Sodium	Protein/Fat
36	Heaven Made	Meat	Scrumptious	0.08	11.75	140	428	1
37	Baked and Smoked	Meat	Scrumptious	0.06	9.49	138	339	1
38	Smart Person Chicken	Poultry	Bland	0.08	10.21	129	430	2
39	Woods Park Chicken	Poultry	Medium	0.05	6.37	132	375	2
40	Tony Turkey	Poultry	Medium	0.07	8.42	102	396	3
41	Rose Garden Turkey	Poultry	Medium	0.08	9.37	106	383	3

The HOTDOGS table has the following information:

- The columns called Type, Calories, Sodium, and Protein/Fat (an index ratio of protein to fat) give information about nutrition. The Type column has values "Meat," "Poultry," and "Beef."
- Cost information is in columns $/oz (dollars per ounce of hotdog) and $lb Prot (dollars per pound of hotdog protein).
- Three categories of taste are coded "Bland," Medium," and "Scrumptious" in the Taste column.

Grouping Data

Health is the first concern of the nutritionist, who wonders if type of hotdog plays a role in healthfulness. In particular, the nutritionist wants to know

- which type of hotdog has the fewest calories
- if the amount of sodium is different in the three types of hotdog
- which hotdogs have the most acceptable protein content
- which hotdogs taste good and are not health risks.

To address these issues, the data need to be grouped into hotdog types and taste preference categories with statistical averages computed for each group. The **Group/Summary** command in the **Tables** menu is the JMP facility for grouping data and computing summary statistics.

Group/Summary creates a JMP window that contains a *summary table*. This table summarizes columns from the active data table, called its *source table*. The HOTDOG table is the source table in this example. A summary table has a single row for each level (value) of a specified variable.

2   The nutritionist selects the **Group/Summary** command to summarize by type of hotdog, and completes the dialog as shown in **Figure 3.2**.

Figure 3.2 The Group/Summary Dialog

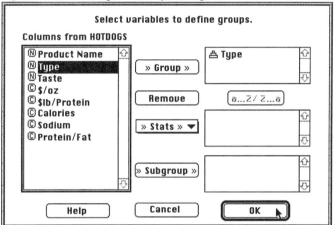

After clicking **Done**, the **Hotdogs by Type** summary table (**Figure 3.3**) appears in a new window. The Type column lists hotdog type, and the N Rows column gives the source table frequency of each type.

Note→ A summary table is not independent of its source table. It has the following characteristics:

- When you highlight rows in the summary table, the corresponding rows highlight in its source table. If the By–Mode button in the upper left corner of the table is on, commands from the **Analyze** and **Graph** menus recognize subsets identified by selected rows in the summary table and produce an analysis window for each subset.

- There is a dollar sign ($) pop–up menu at the lower left of the table display window. This option accesses the Group/Summary dialog so you can add statistical summary columns to the table at any time.

- The summary table is not saved when you close it. However, if you use the **Save As** command to specify a name and location for the table, JMP creates a standard data table from the summary table.

Figure 3.3 Summary Table for Type of Hotdog

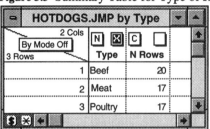

Creating Statistics for Groups

Next, the nutritionist expands the summary table with columns of statistics. To follow along with this example

- use the **Add Summary Cols** command in the dollar ($) menu at the lower left border of the summary table to again display the Group/Summary dialog
- select (SHIFT–click) Calories, Sodium, and Prot/Fat in the column selector list of the dialog
- click the **Stats** pop–up icon on the dialog and select **Mean**
- release the mouse to see new column names listed to the right of the **Stats** pop–up icon as shown in **Figure 3.4.**

Figure 3.4 Summary Table for Type of Hotdog

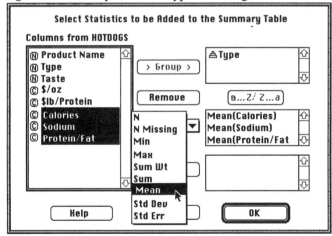

When the nutritionist clicks **Done**, additional columns of statistics show in the **Hotdogs by Type** table (top table of **Figure 3.5**).

Following the previous steps, the nutritionist creates a second summary table and looks at the health factors and hotdog tastiness. The **Hotdogs by Taste** summary table shows average calories, sodium, and protein–to–fat ratio for each taste category (bottom table of **Figure 3.5**).

Figure 3.5 Summary Statistics for Hotdog Groups

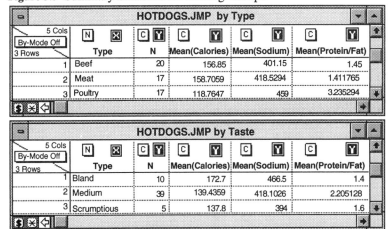

Charting Statistics from Grouped Data

The summary tables in **Figure 3.5** show the summary statistics in tabular form, but bar charts would give an effective visual comparison. Summary tables are especially useful for generating charts.

The nutritionist wants to see bar charts of the nutritional means for each type of hotdog and each taste category. The **Graph** menu has the **Bar/Pie Charts** command designed for charting grouped data.

7   The N column does not play a role in charting summary statistics. The nutritionist changes its role to **None** in both tables, using the role assignment pop–up menu at the top of the column (see **Figure 3.6**).

The grouping variable, Type, was automatically assigned as X in the summary table. The columns of summary statistics were assigned the Y role. **Bar/Pie Charts** produces a bar for each value (level) of the X variable. The size of a bar is proportional to its Y value.

8   The next step the nutritionist takes is to select the **Bar/Pie Charts** command with the **Hotdogs by Type** table active and again with the **Hotdogs by Taste** table active. **Bar/Pie Charts** produces the charts in **Figure 3.7**

Figure 3.6 Role Assignments and the Bar/Pie Charts Command

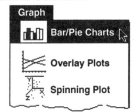

9   The nutritionist uses the **Title** command in the star (∗) pop–up menu and types chart titles as shown in **Figure 3.7**. Display options in the check (✓) pop–up menu arrange the charts horizontally on the page.

Figure 3.7 Bar Charts for Nutrition Content in Types of Hotdogs

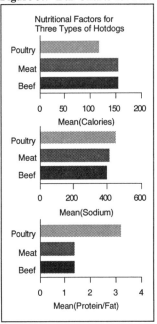 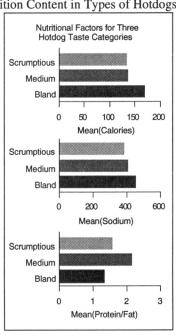

What can be said about health factors and type of hotdog?

It appears that poultry hotdogs have fewer calories on the average than the other two hotdog types. But the nutritionist also notes that the poultry hotdogs have slightly more sodium. The most visible difference is that the protein–to–fat ratio appears much higher in poultry hotdogs.

What can be said about health factors and taste of hotdog?

The nutritionist is surprised to see that hotdogs rated as bland tasting have (on the average) more calories, more sodium, and a lower protein–to–fat ratio. Scrumptious tasting hotdogs have the lowest average calories and sodium content. However, medium tasting hotdogs have the highest protein–to–fat ratio, and they compare well with respect to the other nutritional factors.

Charting Statistics for Two Groups

10 Next, it is useful to know the frequency of the three taste responses for each type of hotdog. The nutritionist uses **Group/Summary** again and selects both Type and Taste as grouping variables, which produces the table in **Figure 3.8**. There is one row for each taste response within each type of hotdog. The N Rows column lists the frequency in the source table of each type–taste combination.

Figure 3.8 Hotdogs Grouped by Type and by Taste

HOTDOGS.JMP by Type Taste

3 Cols / By-Mode Off / 9 Rows	Type	Taste	N Rows
1	Beef	Bland	3
2	Beef	Medium	16
3	Beef	Scrumptious	1
4	Meat	Bland	6
5	Meat	Medium	8
6	Meat	Scrumptious	3
7	Poultry	Bland	1
8	Poultry	Medium	15
9	Poultry	Scrumptious	1

11 The **Group/Summary** command automatically assigns both grouping variables the X role. Initially, the N Rows column is assigned the Y role. The **Bar/Pie Charts** command produces the charts shown in **Figure 3.9**. In this example there are side–by–side taste charts for each hotdog type.

Figure 3.9 Frequency Bar Charts for Two Grouping Variables

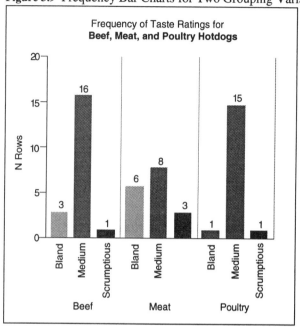

12 To label each bar with the frequency it represents, the nutritionist uses the **Select All Rows** command followed by the **Label/Unlabel** command in the **Rows** menu.

The poultry hotdogs excelled in nutrition factors (**Figure 3.9**), and the nutritionist notes with interest that most people found them medium tasting. However, because the sodium content appeared slightly high in some poultry brands, more investigation is needed.

Finding a Subgroup with Multiple Characteristics

13 The **Clear Row States** command in the **Rows** menu removes the labels from the source table rows (and the bar charts), and deselects the rows. This prepares the summary table, **Hotdogs by Type Taste**, for assignment of special markers to identify each type of hotdog.

Clear the row states in your table, and complete the following steps to see how the nutritionist continues in search of the ideal hotdog.

In the Type–Taste summary table

- shift–click the medium and scrumptious beef rows (2 and 3) to select them. Use the **Markers** command in the **Rows** menu to assign them the **Z** marker and then deselect those rows.
- shift–click the medium and scrumptious meat rows (5 and 6) to select them, assign them the **Y** marker, and deselect them.
- shift–click the medium and scrumptious poultry rows (8 and 9), assign them the **X** marker, and deselect them

The Type–Taste summary table now looks like this:

Figure 3.10 Groups Identified with Row State Markers

	HOTDOGS.JMP by Type Taste		
3 Cols By-Mode Off 9 Rows		Type	Taste
	1	Beef	Bland
z	2	Beef	Medium
z	3	Beef	Scrumptious
	4	Meat	Bland
Y	5	Meat	Medium
Y	6	Meat	Scrumptious
	7	Poultry	Bland
x	8	Poultry	Medium
x	9	Poultry	Scrumptious

Comparative Scatterplots

The nutritionist wants to examine the relevant variables with scatter plots to identify specific points (brands). The **FIT Y BY X** command in the **Analyze** menu produces scatterplots when both the X and Y are continuous variables. The cost and nutritional content variables are numeric columns. Use the pop–up menu at the top of each column in the source table and select **Continuous** as the modeling type for these columns.

Note➡ The Prot/Fat variable is numeric but was used as an ordinal variable in the previous plots. Now it must be changed to continuous.

15 The following scatterplots show graphically the relationship of cost and the nutritional factors together. Click the HOTDOGS source table to make it active, and create scatterplots as follows:

- Select the **Fit Y by X** command and complete the role assignment dialog giving $/lb Protein the Y role and both $/oz and Prot/Fat the X role. This produces $/lb Protein by $/oz and a $/lb Prot by Prot/Fat scatterplots.

- For each scatterplot select the **Grouping Variable** command in the fitting pop–up menu below the plot. Complete the dialog to assign Type as the grouping variable.

- After selecting the grouping variable, choose the **Density Ellipses** option. Select .90 ellipses as shown to the right in **Figure 3.11**.

Complete the same actions with Calories as Y and Sodium as X. These commands produce the $/lb Prot by $/oz, the $/lb Protein by Protein/Fat, and the Calories by Sodium scatterplots shown in **Figure 3.12**.

Figure 3.11 Fitting Pop–up Menu Commands for Scatterplots

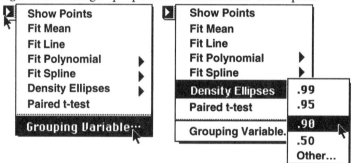

The 90% ellipses in the scatterplots show the shape of the bivariate response for each type of hotdog. The special markers identify the taste and type of each point.

To further identify points, the nutritionist selects the brush tool from the **Tools** menu. Holding down the option key and dragging the brush highlights the points in the lower left quadrant of the Calories by Sodium scatterplot, as shown on the right in **Figure 3.12**. These points represent brands with both low sodium and low calories. The highlighted points of these healthiest brands also highlight in the other scatterplots.

Figure 3.12 Scatterplots Comparing Cost, Taste, and Nutritional Factors

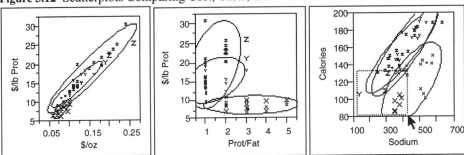

**What can be said
...about cost?**
The costs of meat and beef brands ranges from low to high. However, the nutritionist is not surprised to see the tight low–cost cluster of poultry brands (X–marked) at the lower left of the $/lb Protein by $/oz scatterplot. The highlighted points include poultry brands, one meat brand, and one beef brand. The selected beef point (Z–marked) is in the upper right corner of the plot, which places it in the most expensive category. The single meat point (Y–marked) is more costly than the poultry brands but less than the beef brands.

**...about protein cost
and the ratio of
protein to fat?**
A bigger surprise appears in the $/lb Protein by Protein/Fat scatterplot. As the protein to fat ratio increases, the cost per pound of protein decreases. Further, the poultry brands not only cost the least, but also contain the most protein. Most of the selected points are in the three highest protein categories.

**...about calories
and sodium?**
The density ellipses on the Calories by Sodium scatterplot show clearly that the poultry brands have about the same range of sodium content as the meat and beef brands, but many poultry brands have fewer calories.

Finding the Best Points

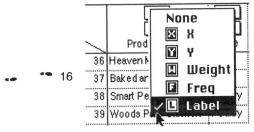

Now there is sufficient information to identify several hotdog brands as possible cafeteria menu items. The nutritionist clicks the HOTDOGS table to make it active and assigns the Product Name as a Label column with the role assignment pop–up menu, as shown to the left.

The poultry (X–marked) brands are acceptably economical and some of them have high protein content. Few meat or beef brands compared well. However, in fairness and curiosity, the nutritionist clicks the

Calories by Sodium scatterplot to deselect all points, and then shift–clicks to highlight

- the two poultry brands with the least calories and lowest sodium content
- the lone meat point (**Y**–marked) that has the least sodium of all brands, is low in calories, has a moderate protein count, and is average in price.

17 The **Label/Unlabel** command in the **Rows** menu displays the brand names of highlighted points (Thin Jack Veal, Calorie–less Turkey, and Estate Chicken) as shown in **Figure 3.13**.

Figure 3.13 Labels of Ideal Points

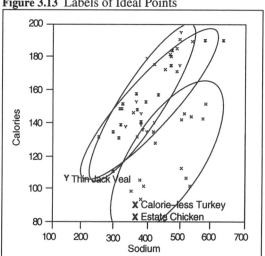

18 As a final step the nutritionist uses the **Fit Y by X** command to look again at the two scatterplots that compare costs. The plot to the left in **Figure 3.14** shows that the Estate Chicken brand is the most economical of the three labeled brands. The plot to the right indicates that the Calorie–less Turkey brand is in the group with the highest proportion of protein.

The nutritionist feels that the small increase in cost justifies the added nutritional values of the Calorie–less Turkey and chooses that brand to be the new official cafeteria hotdog.

Figure 3.14 The Winning Hotdog Brands

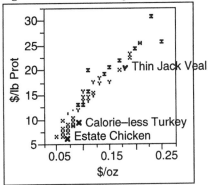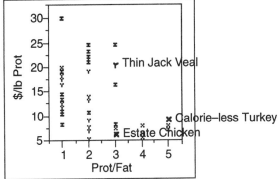

<hr>

Chapter Summary

A nutritionist is responsible for choosing a hotdog brand for a cafeteria menu. A JMP table has data for 54 brands of hotdog showing type of hotdog, taste preference, nutritional factors, and cost factors.

To find the ideal hotdog the nutritionist

- creates summary tables that group the data by hotdog type, by taste preference, and by taste preference within each hotdog type
- uses the **Bar/Pie Charts** command in the **Graph** menu to chart summary statistics and identify the subset of hotdog brands that are both the most nutritious and the best tasting
- assigns different markers to each type of hotdog
- uses **Fit Y by X** in the **Analyze** menu to see scatterplots that compare cost factors and nutritional factors
- selects the lowest costing most nutritious points and uses the **Label/Unlabel** command in the **Rows** menu to identify the "Calorie–less Turkey" brand as the new standard cafeteria hotdog.

See Chapter 4, "Manipulating Tables: The **Tables** Menu," in the *JMP User's Guide* for details about the **Group/Summary** Command.

Chapter 3, "Simple Regression and Curve Fitting," and Chapter 18, "Bar, Line, and Pie Charts," in the *JMP Statistics and Graphics Guide* show scatterplot and bar chart examples.

Chapter 4
Looking at Distributions

School Health
Study

The students in a local school are participating in a health study. The data analyst for the school system has been asked to summarize basic information about the students for the school system health care specialists. The data collected include age, sex, weight, and height.

Data summaries are needed to document the sample of participating students and identify any students with unusual characteristics who may need special medical attention. The job of the analyst is to produce these reports with graphs and short, straightforward explanations.

You can follow the path the analyst takes to summarize demographic information and health data. The data are in the JMP file called STUDENTS, found in the SAMPLE DATA folder. If you are using Windows, the file is called students.jmp and is in the data folder. When you open a Windows file the spreadsheet view appears in uppercase letters (STUDENTS.JMP).

Look Before You Leap

The school analyst knows that the first step is to become familiar with the data in the STUDENTS (students.jmp) file. Looking at the information in the JMP spreadsheet helps the analyst decide which summary charts and tables to use in the health report.

Open a JMP File

1 To view the STUDENTS spreadsheet, use either of these methods:
   - Double–click the JMP icon and then use the **Open** command in the **File** menu to open the JMP file called STUDENTS (or students.jmp).
   - Double–click the STUDENTS (students.jmp) file icon to start the JMP application automatically and display the STUDENTS spreadsheet.

You should see the spreadsheet shown in **Figure 4.1**.

Figure 4.1 The STUDENTS Spreadsheet

5 Cols / 233 Rows	age	sex	height	weight	idnum
1	11	F	56	85	874
2	11	F	57	69	31
3	11	F	54	69	613
4	11	F	62	104	814
5	11	F	51	51	628
6	11	F	62	85	895

The file contains the height, weight, age, sex and an identification number for each student participating in the health study. The data table is in order by age, and sex is ordered within each age group.

Even though there are only five columns of information, these variables address the following questions that interest the health researchers:

- How many boys and how many girls are there?
- How old are they?
- What is the average height and weight for the group?

- Are there any students much younger or older than the average age?
- Are there any students whose height or weight might signal the need for medical attention?

Choose Variable Roles

2

The school analyst begins by examining the demographic distribution (age and sex) of the students. To identify the columns for analysis, the analyst assigns the role of **Y** to both the age and sex columns. The empty box at the top of each column is a pop–up role assignment menu.

Figure 4.2 Choose Variable Roles

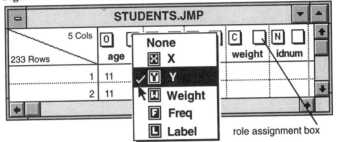

Note➡ You can examine as many or as few columns as you like during a JMP session. When you assign the role of **Y** to a column, you cast it as a response variable for the analysis. As the investigation proceeds, you can change the role of a variable or select **None** from the pop–up menu to eliminate the column from further analysis.

Graphical Display of Distributions

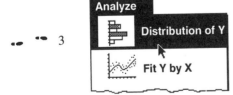

3

Now the analyst is ready to select a command from the **Analyze** menu to summarize the data, and selects the **Distribution of Y** command, as shown to the left. Each column identified as a **Y** variable (response) for the analysis is summarized individually.

Histograms of Nominal and Ordinal Values

Distribution of Y displays histograms for each **Y** column. The histogram for ordinal or nominal variables like age and sex has a bar for each level (value) of the variable. Display options (described later) let you see additional plots and graphs such as the mosaic bar chart to the right of the histogram in **Figure 4.3**.

Figure 4.3 Histogram and Mosaic Bar Chart of the Age Variable

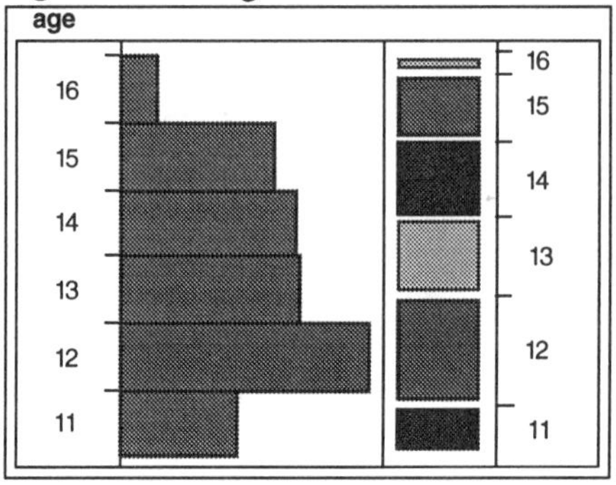

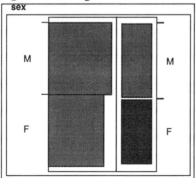

What can be said about age?   The analyst sees at a glance that the distribution of age is slightly skewed with a larger proportion of younger students and fewer older students.

Figure 4.4 Histogram and Mosaic Chart of the Sex Variable

What can be said about gender?   The bars for sex appear nearly the same. The proportion of boys and girls in the school is about even, which is what you expect to see.

Histograms of Continuous Values

4   The analyst continues by looking at the distribution of height and weight values in the sample of students. To follow along with the analyst, click the STUDENTS spreadsheet to make it the active window. Using the role assignment box on the spreadsheet, designate the height and weight columns as response variables (**Y**). Designate the age and sex columns as **None** to eliminate them from the next analysis. **Distribution of Y** displays the plots for height and weight as shown in **Figure 4.5**.

Figure 4.5 Histograms of Height and Weight

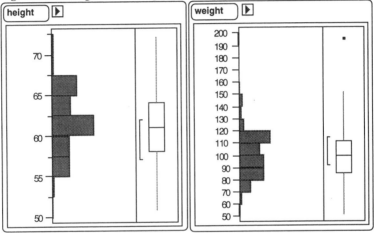

What can be said about height and weight?

Both height and weight appear to have approximately normal (bell–shaped) distributions, but the analyst notices an extremely high weight value and wants to examine it more closely later.

The analyst knows it is important to present data in the best possible form. Sometimes it pays to experiment with the shape of a histogram by changing the number of bars, or their arrangement on the axis.

5   To adjust the histogram bars, select the hand from the **Tools** menu. Position the hand on the bars and hold down the mouse button to *grab* the plot. If you think of each bar as a bin that holds a number of observations, then moving the hand to the left increases the bin width and combines intervals (see **Figure 4.6**). The number of bars decreases as the bar size increases. Moving the hand to the right decreases the bin width showing more bars. Moving the hand up or down changes the boundaries of the bins. The height of each bar adjusts according to the new number of observations within each bin.

Figure 4.6 Adjust the Number of Bars

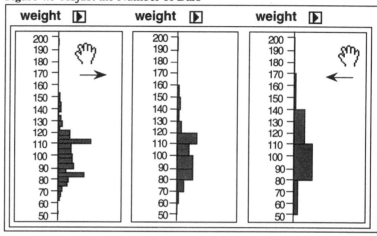

Exchange the hand for the standard arrow cursor in the **Tools** menu after adjusting the bars.

Mosaic Bar Charts for Ordinal and Nominal Variables

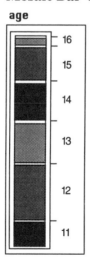

age

The figure to the left is a mosaic chart for the age variable.

For ordinal or nominal variables, a mosaic bar accompanies each frequency histogram. The mosaic bar chart is a way to visualize the proportion of each ordinal or nominal level within the sample. The mosaic bar has a section for each level of the variable, where the size of the section is proportional to the corresponding group's size. You can think of a mosaic chart as a bar chart with its bars stacked end to end.

You can suppress the Mosaic chart by selecting it in the list of display options accessed by the check mark (✓) menu at the lower left of the window. See the section, **Display Options,** later in this chapter for a discussion of options.

Outlier Box Plots for Continuous Variables

The *outlier box plot* (see **Figure 4.7**) is a schematic that lets you see the sample distribution and identify points with extreme values, sometimes called *outliers*.

The ends of the box are the 25th and 75th quantiles, also called the *quartiles*. The difference between the quartiles is the *interquartile range*. The line across the middle of the box identifies the median sample value.

The lines extending from each end of the box are sometimes called *whiskers*. The whiskers extend from the ends of the box to the outermost data points that fall within the distance computed:

quartile $\pm$ 1.5 (interquartile range).

Points beyond the whiskers indicate extreme values that are possible outliers. Points can be identified with the **Label** command in the **Rows** menu as illustrated by point "182" in **Figure 4.7**. To label a point, click on the point to highlight it, and select then select the **Label** command.

The bracket along the edge of the box identifies the *shortest half*, which is the most dense 50% of the observations.

Figure 4.7 Outlier Box Plot

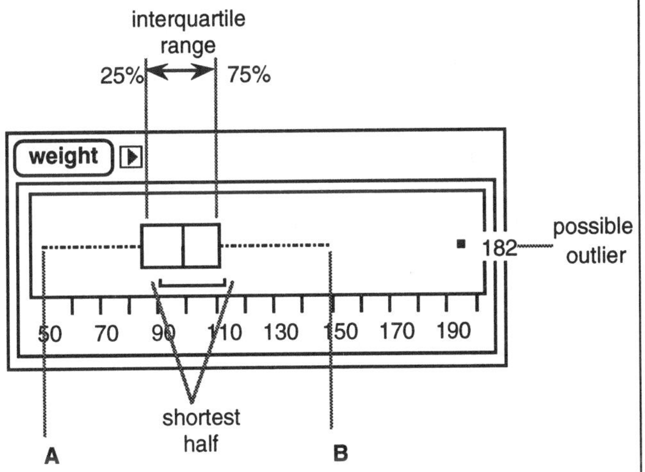

The ends of the whiskers, denoted **A** and **B**, are the outermost data points from their respective quartiles that fall within the distance computed as 1.5 * (interquartile range).

Display Options

⟶ 6 The histogram, mosaic plot, and outlier box plot are optional representations of data that appear by default when you choose the **Distribution of Y** command. The check mark (✓) pop–up menu to the left of the horizontal scroll bar lists other display options (**Figure 4.8**). For example, the **Quantile Box Plot** selection gives the plot shown in **Figure 4.9**.

Figure 4.8 Graphical Display Options

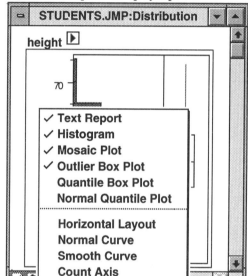

The quantile box plot shows the location of selected percentiles, sometimes called quantiles, on the response axis. The median shows as a line in the body of the box. The ends of the box locate the 25th and 75th quantiles. The number of other quantile lines depends on the available space. The accompanying text report lists the data values for each of the standard quantiles.

The box also contains a means diamond. The two diamond points within the box identify the 95% confidence interval of the mean. The line that passes through the two diamond points spanning the box identifies the sample mean.

Looking at the quantile box plot and means rectangle together helps you to see if data are distributed normally. If data are distributed normally (bell shaped), then the 50th quantile and the mean are the same and other quantiles show symmetrically above and below them.

Figure 4.9 Quantile Box Plot and Quantiles Table

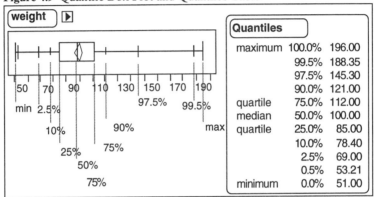

Try different combinations of these options and watch the effect they have on the graphical displays and text reports.

Text Reports

The analyst needs tables of statistical summaries to accompany the graphs. The graphical display option called **Text Report** is a toggle for viewing or hiding text reports buttons. The **Text Report** option displays reveal/conceal buttons showing or hiding each report.

Reports for Continuous Variables

7 The text report JMP produces depends on whether a variable is continuous, ordinal, or nominal. In **Figure 4.10** you see the report for the continuous variable height. The reveal/conceal buttons open the report tables showing Quantiles and Moments:

- The Quantiles table displays the maximum value, minimum value, and other values for selected quantiles.
- The Moments table displays the mean, standard deviation, and other summary statistics.

Figure 4.10 Tables for Continuous Values

height ▶

Quantiles			Moments	
maximum	100.0%	72.000	Mean	61.33047
	99.5%	71.830	Std Dev	3.89825
	97.5%	69.000	Std Err Mean	0.25538
	90.0%	66.000	upper 95% Mean	61.83102
quartile	75.0%	64.000	lower 95% Mean	60.82992
median	50.0%	61.000	N	233
quartile	25.0%	58.000	Sum Wgts	233
	10.0%	56.000		
	2.5%	53.000		
	0.5%	51.000		
minimum	0.0%	51.000		

Note➜ The pop–up menu next to each continuous variable name lets you compare the variable's mean to any constant you specify and gives you a table that shows the resulting *t*–test.

Frequency Table for Ordinal or Nominal Variables

8 The report for nominal and ordinal variables has a different table from those produced for continuous variables. Click the report window showing **sex** and **age** to make it active. Frequency tables like the one in **Figure 4.11** shows beneath the histogram. The Frequency table has the following items:

Level

lists each value found for a response variable.

Count

lists the number of rows found for each level of a response variable.

Probability

lists the probability of occurrence for each level of a response variable. The probability is computed as the count divided by the total frequency of the variable, shown at the bottom of the table.

Cum Prob

contains the cumulative sum of the column of probabilities.

Figure 4.11 The Frequency Table for Ordinal or Nominal Values

Frequencies			
Level	Count	Probability	Cum Prob
11	30	0.12876	0.12876
12	63	0.27039	0.39914
13	46	0.19742	0.59657
14	45	0.19313	0.78970
15	39	0.16738	0.95708
16	10	0.04292	1.00000
Total	233		

Creating a Subset

The health study specialists want to be on the alert for any unusual subjects such as students who have extreme height or weight values. The analyst knows that a good indicator of extreme values is the proportion of weight to height.

Add a Computed Column

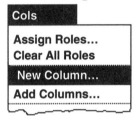

9   To examine the ratio of weight to height, the analyst creates a new column called ratio, computed as weight divided by height. To do this, first click the STUDENTS spreadsheet to make it the active window and select the **New Column** command in the **Cols** Menu as shown to the left.

10   To create the new column of weight/height ratios, complete the new column dialog as shown in **Figure 4.12**.

Figure 4.12 The New Column Dialog

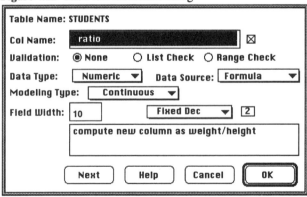

The pop-up menus on the dialog called **Data Type**, **Data Source**, **Modeling Type**, and **Format** let you define the new column's characteristics as follows:

- Type the new name, ratio, in the **Col Name** area.
- The default **Data Type** is **Numeric** and is correct as is.

- Use the **Data Source** pop–up menu and select **Formula** so you can compute values for the new column.
- **Modeling Type** shows as **Continuous** and is correct as is.
- Use the **Format** pop–up menu and set the spreadsheet format for ratio to **Fixed Dec** with two decimal places.
- Type any notes you want into the **Notes** area.

After you click **OK,** the calculator window appears. **Figure 4.13** shows the calculator window and the ratio formula. Construct the formula that calculates values for the ratio column as follows:

1. Select **weight** from the list of column names in the upper left corner of the calculator.
2. Press the divide (÷) key on the calculator keypad.
3. Select **height** from the list of column names.

11

Figure 4.13 The Calculator Window

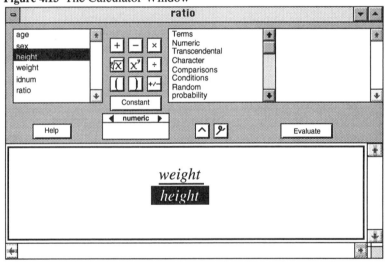

When the formula is complete, click the close box in the upper left corner of the calculator window. The new column called ratio is now in the STUDENTS.JMP data table (**Figure 4.14**). Its values are the computed weight–to–height ratio for each student.

Figure 4.14 Adding a New Column

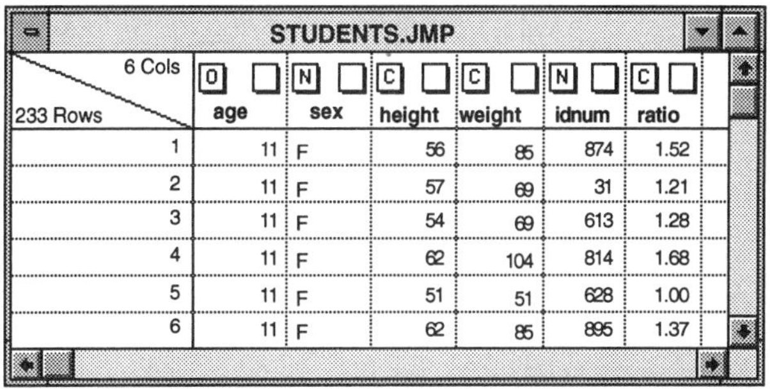

6 Cols	age	sex	height	weight	idnum	ratio
233 Rows						
1	11	F	56	85	874	1.52
2	11	F	57	69	31	1.21
3	11	F	54	69	613	1.28
4	11	F	62	104	814	1.68
5	11	F	51	51	628	1.00
6	11	F	62	85	895	1.37

STUDENTS.JMP

12   Next, the analyst assigns Y as the variable role for ratio and sets all other existing role assignments to **None**. The analyst uses the **Distribution of Y** command in the **Analyze** menu to look at the distribution of the ratios.

13   All that remains is to identify the subjects having extreme values. One way to do this is to highlight histogram bars for the highest and lowest values. To highlight more than one bar, hold down the shift key and click each bar.

Figure 4.15 Histogram of Ratio with End Bars Highlighted

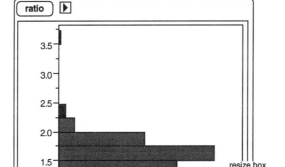

Note➡ In the histogram shown in **Figure 4.15**, the plot frame was resized. To resize any plot click anywhere in the plot to see a small resize box in the lower right corner. Click and drag the box to change the plot size.

Which students
have extreme
values?

In **Figure 4.16**, the highlighted bars represent a ratio either greater than or equal to 2.25 or less than 1.25. The corresponding values automatically highlight in all other reports generated from the STUDENTS data table. The corresponding rows are also automatically selected on the spreadsheet.

Figure 4.16 Selected Rows in the Data Table

	STUDENTS					
6 Cols	O	N	C	C	N	C Y
233 Rows	age	sex	height	weight	idnum	ratio
146	14	F	62	143	56	2.31
147	14	F	63	103	251	1.63
148	14	F	62	95	986	1.53
149	14	F	62	99	723	1.60
150	14	F	61	112	921	1.84
151	14	F	64	149	867	2.33
152	14	F	67	118	687	1.76

Create a New View

The analyst clicks on the STUDENTS spreadsheet to examine the selected rows but finds that scrolling through a large spreadsheet can be tedious. For the final report to the health researchers, the analyst decides to include a separate list containing only the highlighted students.

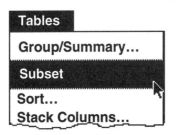

The **Tables** menu commands create new data tables or modify existing tables. Select **Subset** from the **Tables** menu to create a new data table that has only the selected rows and columns from the active data table.

The new spreadsheet, shown in **Figure 4.17**, has the students with extreme weight–to–height ratios. The analyst uses the **Set Window Name** command from the **Window** menu to change the table name from **Untitled 1** to **Subset of Students**. You can save this table as a JMP file, export it for use in another application, or print it from the JMP session.

Figure 4.17 Data Table Containing a Selected Subset

6 Cols / 10 Rows	age	sex	height	weight	idnum	ratio
1	11	F	57	69	31	1.21
2	11	F	51	51	628	1.00
3	11	F	53	64	238	1.21
4	12	F	52	64	804	1.23
5	13	F	56	67	635	1.20
6	13	M	62	140	262	2.26
7	14	F	62	143	56	2.31
8	14	F	64	149	867	2.33
9	14	M	54	196	•	3.63
10	15	M	66	151	710	2.29

Chapter Summary

In this chapter, a school analyst summarized the demographic and vital data of students participating in a health study. The analyst completed the profile using the **Distribution of Y** analysis platform and data management features of the JMP spreadsheet.

The **Distribution of Y** platform displayed histograms and box plots or divided (stacked) bar charts for each variable assigned the role of response variable (Y). Using display and text report options to look more closely at data, the analyst was able to

- adjust the number of bars and the scale of the histograms
- produce supporting statistical reports showing moments and quantiles of numeric variables and frequencies and proportions of nominal and ordinal variables
- create a new column in the data table computed as a function of existing columns
- highlight histogram bars to identify a subset of rows in the data table
- create a new data table from a subset of highlighted rows.

The analyst can print graphs and text reports from JMP. The analyst can copy graphs and reports to a JMP journal or into other applications to complete a report for the school system health care specialists.

See Chapter 2, "Distributions," in the *JMP Statistics and Graphics Guide* for more information about distributions.

Chapter 5
Comparing Group Means

In keeping with a recent corporate policy to modernize operations, all the typewriters in the typing pool are to be replaced with modern word processors. The typists are eager for this change and willingly participated in a study to help decide what kind of equipment to buy. The company selected three different brands of machine to test. The corporate statistician randomly assigned the machines to three groups of typists with comparable typing skills. The typists completed typing tests and recorded their words–per–minute scores.

The corporate statistician is asked to find out if the typing scores are significantly better on any one brand of machine than on the others.

If statistics can show that one machine promotes significantly faster typing than the others, that machine wins the corporate contract and becomes the new company standard. If no such difference can be found, the company will buy the word processor that the employees like best.

Look Before You Leap

The first step is to become familiar with the data. The typing test scores are in a JMP file so that the statistician can review the information and determine the kind of analysis needed.

Open a JMP File

1 The statistician begins a JMP session and opens the file called TYPING DATA in the SAMPLE DATA on the Macintosh (or the typing.jmp in the data folder under Windows). Alternatively, you can double–click the TYPING DATA file to open it and to start JMP running automatically. The TYPING DATA table appears in spreadsheet form as shown in **Figure 5.1**.

Figure 5.1 The Typing Data Table

brand [N]	speed [C]
REGAL	70
SPEEDYTYPE	87
SPEEDYTYPE	79
REGAL	73
SPEEDYTYPE	77
REGAL	72
WORD-O-MATIC	62

The data table has columns called brand and speed. The modeling type for each column shows in the box above the column name. The variable brand has nominal (N) values and speed has continuous (C) values.

There are 17 rows representing typing scores for 17 typists. However, the number of participants in each group differs because some of the scheduled participants did not show up for the study. The statistician wonders if any other statistics for the groups differ also. In particular, the statistician asks,

"Is the mean (average) typing speed the same for each brand?"

Does any one of the three brands of word processor stand out from the others, or does it make no difference which brand the typists use? Because the company intends to make a large investment based on this statistical analysis, the statistician must evaluate the data carefully.

Choose Variable Roles

2 The statistician first assigns variable roles using role assignment pop–up menus as shown in **Figure 5.2**. Select **X** for brand and **Y** for speed to follow along with the statistician.

- Y identifies a response (dependent) variable.
- X identifies a classification (independent) variable.

JMP produces a statistical analysis appropriate for the variable role, the modeling type of each variable, and the selected analysis platform. The next step is to choose an analysis that answers the question,

"Is there a statistical difference between the mean values of Y within the levels of X?"

Figure 5.2 Select X and Y Variables

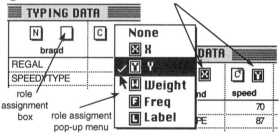

Graphical Display of Grouped Data

3 To compare the mean typing scores of each word processor brand, the statistician selects the **Fit Y by X** command from the **Analyze** menu.

Figure 5.3 The Analyze Menu

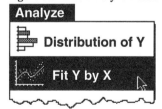

Note➡ **Fit Y by X** can be used for four kinds of analyses:

- categorical analysis when both X and Y have nominal/ordinal values

- analysis of variance when X is nominal/ordinal and Y has continuous values, as in this example
- logistic regression when X is continuous and Y has nominal/ordinal values
- regression analysis when both X and Y have continuous values.

Show Points

After selecting **Fit Y by X** from the **Analyze** menu, the plot shown in **Figure 5.4** appears. Each of the typing test scores is plotted for each brand of word processor. Note that the distance between tick marks on the brand axis is proportional to the sample size of each group. The mean typing score for the total sample is shown as the dotted line across the plot.

Figure 5.4 Scatterplot of Typing Scores

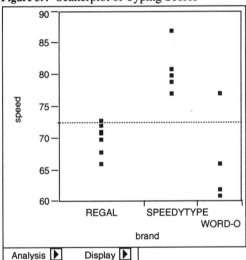

How do the data points look? The statistician sees at a glance that most participants who used the SPEEDYTYPE machines typed faster than the others.

Fit Means Option

The statistician now chooses to look at more graphical information about the distribution of typing scores by using commands from the Analysis and Display pop–up menus accessed by the triangles at the lower left corner of the plot (**Figure 5.5**). Initially, only the **Show Points** and **X-axis Proportional** display options are in effect. The options are *toggles*, meaning you turn any option alternately on and off each time you select it.

4   To follow the path of the statistician, use the Analysis options menu and select **Means, Anova/t-test** from its pop–up menu as shown below.

Figure 5.5 The Analysis and Display Plot Options Menus

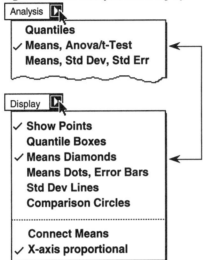

The **Means, Anova/t-test** produces the appropriate analysis of variance reports and automatically selects the **Means Diamonds** option from the Display menu. This option draws a 95% *means diamond* for each group (**Figure 5.6**).

The means diamond has a line drawn at the mean (average) value of words–per–minute for each brand of word processor. The upper and lower points of the means diamond span a 95% confidence interval computed from the sample values for each machine.

Figure 5.6 Example of The Means Diamonds Option

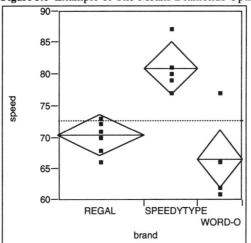

The illustration in **Figure 5.7** describes the means diamond. The difference in the number of group participants displays as a difference in diamond width with larger sample sizes having wider means lines. The width of each diamond spans the distance on the horizontal axis proportional to the group size.

Figure 5.7 The Means Diamond

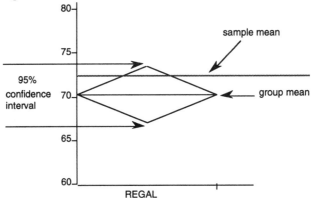

How do the means compare?   The mean scores of the REGAL and WORD–O word processors appear to be nearly the same, but the statistician sees that the SPEEDYTYPE mean is much higher.

Fit Quantiles

5 The statistician wants to check the distribution of points within each group to get a better idea of the spread of the values and to visualize the distance of extreme values from the center of the data. The **Quantiles** option in the Analysis pop–up menu is useful for making this comparison. **Quantiles** displays the report in **Figure 5.8**, which lists the standard percentiles for each word processor.

Figure 5.8 The Quantiles Table

Quantiles	minimum	10.0%	25.0%	median	75.0%	90.0%	maximum
Level							
REGAL	66	66	68.5	70.5	72	73	73
SPEEDYTYPE	77	77	78	80	84	87	87
WORD-O-MATIC	61	61	61.25	64	74.25	77	77

The **Quantiles** analysis option automatically selects the **Quantile Boxes** display option, which overlays a quantile box plot on each group of typing scores as shown in **Figure 5.9**.

Figure 5.9 The Fit Quantiles Option

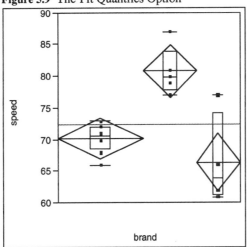

Figure 5.10 illustrates the quantile box plot. The median, or 50th quantile, shows as a line in the body of the box. The top and bottom of the box represent the 75th and 25th quantiles, also called the upper and lower quartiles. The box encompasses the *interquartile range* of the sample data. The 10th and 90th quantiles show as lines above and below each box .

Looking at the quantile box plot and the means rectangle together helps you to see if data are distributed normally within a group. If data are normally distributed (bell shaped), the 50th percentile and the mean are the same and the other quantiles are arranged symmetrically above and below the median.

Figure 5.10 The Quantiles Box Plot

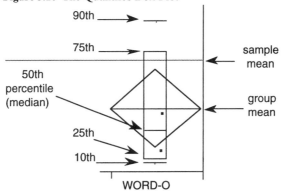

How are the typing scores distributed within each brand? The quantile box plots show there is a difference in variation of scores across the three groups. The scores in the REGAL group cluster tightly around the mean score but the WORD–O scores vary. One WORD–O score is much higher than the others. However, even with this variation among the groups, the SPEEDYTYPE brand still appears to promote the best performance.

Comparison Circles

6   To complete the typing data inspection, the statistician chooses **Compare All Pairs** from the Analysis pop–up menu. This option produces statistical reports (discussed later) and automatically selects the **Comparison Circles** option in the Display pop–up menu. A set of *comparison circles* displayed to the right of the plot provide a graphic test of whether the mean typing scores are statistically different. Comparison circles for the three word–processor groups show in **Figure 5.11**.

The center of each circle is aligned with the mean of the group it represents. The diameter of each circle spans the 95 percent confidence interval for each group. Whenever two circles intersect, the confidence intervals of the two means overlap, suggesting that the means may not be significantly different. Whenever two circles do not intersect, the group means they represent are significantly different.

By clicking the SPEEDYTYPE comparison circle, the statistician sees that the SPEEDYTYPE machine is statistically better than the other machines. The confidence circles highlight to show the statistical magnitude of the difference between typing scores. Circles for groups that are statistically the same have the same color and pattern.

Figure 5.11 Comparison Circles

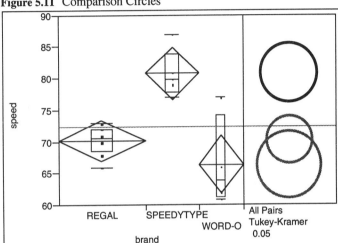

Are the mean typing scores different? You can see that the confidence circle for the SPEEDYTYPE brand does not intersect with either of the other two. The REGAL and WORD-O brands are statistically slower than SPEEDYTYPE but do not appear different from each other. The next section discusses the multiple comparison tests the comparison circles represent.

Quantify Results

7 The **Means, Anova/t-test** command produces the Means report beneath the plot, which consists of several tables. The Summary of Fit table, shown in **Figure 5.12**, summarizes the typing data distribution.

Figure 5.12 Summary of Fit Table

Summary of Fit	
RSquare	0.67446
RSquare Adj	0.627954
Root Mean Square Error	4.27033
Mean of Response	72.47059
Observations (or Sum Wgts)	17

The Summary of Fit table lists the following statistics:

- Rsquare quantifies the proportion of total variation in the typing scores resulting from different word processors rather than from different people.
- Rsquare Adj adjusts Rsquare to make it more comparable over models with different numbers of parameters.
- Root Mean Square Error (RMSE) is a measure of the variation in the typing scores that can be attributed to different people rather than to different machines.
- Mean of Response is the mean (average) of all the typing scores.
- Observations is the total number of scores recorded.

Analysis of Variance

The table shown in **Figure 5.13** is a standard analysis of variance table. If there are only two group levels, the Means report also includes the t–test table that corresponds to the Analysis of Variance table.

The statistician notes that the value of the F probability is .0004. This implies that the differences observed in this typing trial are expected only 4 times in 10,000 similar trials if the word processors did not really promote different typing performances.

Figure 5.13 Analysis of Variance Table

Analysis of Variance				
Source	DF	Sum of Squares	Mean Square	F Ratio
Model	2	528.93529	264.468	14.5027
Error	14	255.30000	18.236	Prob>F
C Total	16	784.23529		0.0004

The Analysis of Variance table has the following computations:

- **Source** lists the sources of variation, Model, Error, and C Total.
- **DF** lists the degrees of freedom associated with the three sources of variation.
- **Sum of Squares** (SS for short) identifies the sources of variation in the typing scores. C Total is the corrected total SS. It divides (partitions) into the SS for Model and SS for Error.

  The model SS is the variation in the typing scores explained by the analysis of variance model, hypothesizing that the word processors are different.

  The error SS is the remaining or unexplained variation.

- **Mean Square** is the sum of squares divided by its associated degrees of freedom (**DF**).
- **F ratio** is the model mean square divided by the error mean square.

- **Prob > F** is the probability of a greater F value occurring if the mean typing scores for the word processors differed only because different people were typing on them rather than because the word processors themselves differed in any way.

Mean Estimates and Statistical Comparisons

9 To see the list of means for each group, the statistician looks at the Means for Oneway Anova table (**Figure 5.14**). This table summarizes the scores for each brand and tells the statistician the level of performance to expect.

Figure 5.14 The Means for Oneway Anova Table

Means for Oneway Anova			
Level	Number	Mean	Std Error
REGAL	8	70.2500	1.5098
SPEEDYTYPE	5	80.8000	1.9097
WORD-O-MATIC	4	66.5000	2.1352
Note: Std Error uses a pooled estimate of error variance			

The Means for Oneway Anova table shows the following information:

- **Level** lists the name of each group.
- **Number** is the number of scores in each group.
- **Mean** is the mean of each group.
- **Std Error** is the standard error of each group mean.

The **Compare All Pairs** command performs a statistical means comparison for the three pairs of means using the *Tukey–Kramer HSD* (honestly significant difference) test (Tukey 1953, Kramer 1956). The means comparison method compares the actual difference between group means with the difference that would be significantly different. The difference needed for statistical significance is called the LSD (least significant difference).

The graphical results show as the comparison circles previously seen in **Figure 5.11**. The circles' centers represent the actual difference in the group means.

Click the **Means Comparisons** reveal button at the bottom of the text reports to see the table in **Figure 5.15**. The Means Comparisons table shows the actual absolute difference between each means and the LSD. The top half of the report gives information based on a student's t comparison of each pair. The bottom half shows the results of the Tukey–Kramer multiple comparison tests. Pairs with a positive value are significantly different. The statistician uses the Means Comparison table to confirm the visual results in **Figure 5.11**.

Figure 5.15 The Means Comparisons Table

Means Comparisons			
Dif=Mean[i]-Mean[j]	SPEEDYTYPE	REGAL	WORD-O-MATIC
SPEEDYTYPE	0.0000	10.5500	14.3000
REGAL	-10.5500	0.0000	3.7500
WORD-O-MATIC	-14.3000	-3.7500	0.0000

Alpha=   0.05
Comparisons for all pairs using Tukey-Kramer HSD

q*			
2.61728			
Abs(Dif)-LSD	SPEEDYTYPE	REGAL	WORD-O-MATIC
SPEEDYTYPE	-7.06873	4.17833	6.80247
REGAL	4.17833	-5.58833	-3.09427
WORD-O-MATIC	6.80247	-3.09427	-7.90309

Positive values show pairs of means that are significantly different.

Chapter Summary

In this chapter, a corporate statistician summarized the difference in mean typing scores for three brands of word processor. The statistician used the **Fit Y by X** command in the **Analyze** menu to

- plot the typing scores for the three brands of word processor
- overlay a means diamond on each group of typing scores to compare the means of each group
- overlay a quantile box plot on each group of typing scores to compare the shape of the distribution of scores in each group
- produce confidence circles to visualize the difference in mean typing scores
- compute and display a one–way analysis of variance table, which confirmed that at least one pair of means is statistically different
- display a table of the group means and standard errors
- display a table showing the multiple comparison statistical test results for group means.

Using the scissors tool from the **Tools** menu, the statistician can copy the graphs or tables and prepare a report for the corporate decision makers. The report concludes that, in this typing trial, the SPEEDYTYPE word processor produced significantly higher scores than either of the other two brands.

See Chapter 4, "One–Way Layout," in the *JMP Statistics and Graphics Guide* for a complete discussion of one–way analysis of variance.

Chapter 6
Analyzing Categorical Data

Survey data are frequently categorical data rather than measurement data. Analysis of categorical data begins by simply counting the number of responses in categories and subcategories. Counting is easy, but interpreting the relationship between categories based on counts is more complex. It requires computing probabilities and evaluating the likelihood of these probabilities compared to expectations.

For example, an American automobile manufacturer — feeling the pinch of competition from foreign auto sales — has decided to do a market analysis before proceeding with a multimillion–dollar advertising campaign. With this analysis in mind, the auto manufacturer contracts with a market researcher to survey a random sample of people. The auto manufacturer wants to know each participant's age, sex, marital status and auto information. The auto information consists of the manufacturing country, the car's size, and the car's type, whether it is a family, work or sporty car. Using this information, the market researcher hopes to provide the advertising experts with direction for the upcoming advertising campaign.

In particular, the market researcher wants to know more about relationships between car characteristics and the demographic information collected in the sample. In other words . . .

Who buys what?

Look Before You Leap

The first step is to become familiar with the data. The car survey data are in a JMP file called CAR POLL in the SAMPLE DATA folder.

Open a Data Table

1 The market researcher begins a JMP session and opens the CAR POLL file in the SAMPLE DATA folder on the Macintosh (carpoll.jmp file in the data folder under Windows). Alternatively, you can double–click the CAR POLL icon to launch JMP automatically. The CAR POLL data table displays in spreadsheet form as shown in **Figure 6.1**.

Figure 6.1 The CAR POLL Data Table

The CAR POLL data were collected from a random sample of people in a specific geographic area. Age is a numeric variable and is assigned the continuous (C) modeling type. The other five columns are character variables with nominal (N) modeling types.

Address the Research Question

The basic research question asks,

> "Is the response probability for country of manufacture, size of car, or type of car a function of the age, sex, or marital status of the owner?"

The market researcher looks at the spreadsheet to see what specific relationships lend insight into this question. The relationships between the following automobile characteristics and demographics are of interest:

- manufacturing country by age
- manufacturing country by sex
- manufacturing country by marital status
- size of car by age

- size of car by sex
- size of car by marital status
- type of car by age
- type of car by sex
- type of car by marital status.

Modify the Data Table

From past experience, the market researcher feels that better summary information can be obtained from age groups rather than specific ages. In fact, dividing people into two age groups is often the basis for a valuable broad analysis. The market researcher wants to find the median age, which divides the sample into two equal age groups.

Find the Median Age   The distribution of a variable and its corresponding quantiles often shows a good way to form sample groups. The market researcher can use the distribution of the age column to find a reasonable value of age that divides the sample into two groups. To find the age distribution,

- assign age the role of Y using the role assignment pop–up menu at the top of the column
- select the **Distribution of Y** command from the **Analyze** menu as shown in **Figure 6.2**.

Figure 6.2 Look at the Distribution of Age

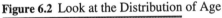

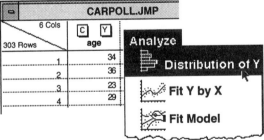

Distribution of Y displays a histogram with its accompanying quantile box plot and Quantiles table. The quantiles table, shown in **Figure 6.3**, identifies 30 as the median age.

Figure 6.3 Quantiles Table for Age

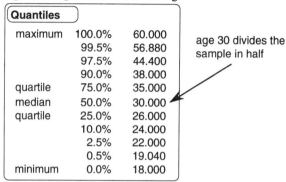

Quantiles			
maximum	100.0%	60.000	age 30 divides the
	99.5%	56.880	sample in half
	97.5%	44.400	
	90.0%	38.000	
quartile	75.0%	35.000	
median	50.0%	30.000	
quartile	25.0%	26.000	
	10.0%	24.000	
	2.5%	22.000	
	0.5%	19.040	
minimum	0.0%	18.000	

4 To create a new column the market researcher selects the **New Column** command from the **Cols** menu. This displays the New Column dialog, shown in **Figure 6.5**, used to define column characteristics.

create a new **Figure 6.4** The New Column Command
column

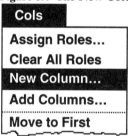

Cols
Assign Roles...
Clear All Roles
New Column...
Add Columns...
Move to First

5 Entries in the dialog fields and the three pop–up menus called **Data Type**, **Data Source**, and **Modeling Type** define the new column's characteristics. You can enter characteristics for the new column in the New Column dialog as follows:

- Type the new name, call it age(50%), in the **Col Name** area.
- Because the new column has grouping values instead of measurements, select **Character** from the **Data Type** pop–up menu . The **Nominal** selection in the **Modeling Type** pop–up menu shows automatically when the data type is character.
- Select **Formula** from the **Data Source** pop–up menu so that you can compute values for the new column.
- Type column documentation notes in the **Notes** area.

Figure 6.5 The New Column Dialog

Table Name: **CARPOLL**

Col Name: **age(50%)**   ☒ **Lock**

Validation: ⦿ **None**   ◯ **List Check**   ◯ **Range Check**

Data Type: **Character** ▾   Data Source: **Formula** ▾

Modeling Type: **Nominal** ▾

Field Width: **10**

Notes: **Date of Birth**

[**Help**]   [**Next**]   [**Cancel**]   [**OK**]

The calculator appears (see **Figure 6.6**) when the researcher clicks **OK**. The researcher chooses "0" and "1" to code the two age groups. To create a formula that divides the sample into two groups using this code and the median age as the dividing point, enter the formula.

$$\begin{cases} \text{"0"}, & \text{if } age < 30 \\ \text{"1"}, & \text{otherwise} \end{cases}$$

Note→ Alternatively, the calculator automatically computes the median age with the formula

$$\begin{cases} \text{"0"}, & \text{if } age < \text{quantile}_{.50}(age) \\ \text{"1"}, & \text{otherwise} \end{cases}$$

Use the following calculator instructions to enter the first formula shown above:

- Scroll through the function browser and click function category called **Conditions.**
- Click **If** in the list of conditions.
- Click the missing term (the empty box) to the left of the word **If**.
- Click the box below the **Constant** button, scroll to see the **character** data type, enter 0, and click the **Constant** button.

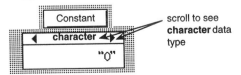

Constant

◀ character ◀▸◀

"0"

scroll to see
character data
type

6...

- Click the missing term (the empty box) to the right of the word if.
- Click age in the column selector list.
- Click Comparisons in the function browser list and select the comparison x < y. This displays the expression *age* < missing term.
- Click the box below the Constant button, scroll to see the **numeric** data type, enter 30, and click the Constant button. The 30 appears in the right–hand comparison box to complete the expression, age<30. The if expression assigns "0" to the new column age(50%) whenever age is less than 30, the median age.
- Click the missing term (the empty box) to the left of the word otherwise.
- Enter a character "1" into the constant box and click the Constant button. The "1" appears in the box to the left of the word otherwise. The otherwise expression assigns "1" to the new column age(50%) whenever age is greater than or equal to 30, the median age.

Click the calculator window's close box to fill the new column with calculated values.

Figure 6.6 The Calculator Window

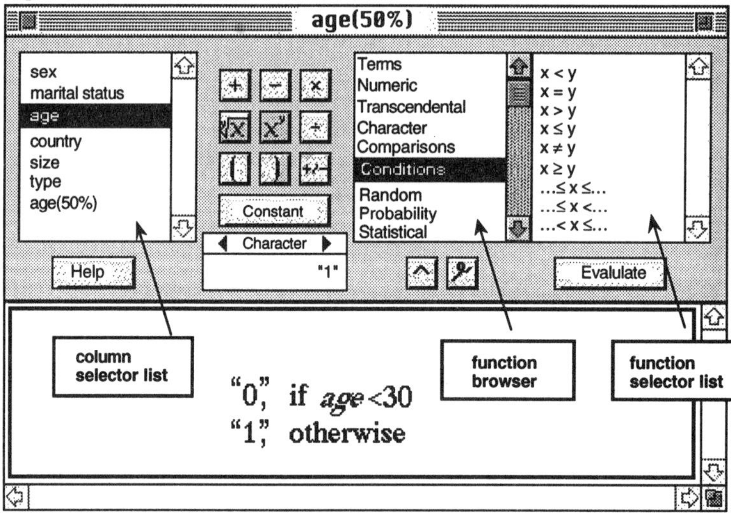

The market researcher is now ready to look at relationships between the variables in the CAR POLL data table.

Contingency Table Reports

7 The nominal age grouping variable lets the analyst look at the relationship of age to the other nominal variables using contingency tables. To look at combinations of two variables, the market researcher chooses the **Fit Y by X** command from the **Analyze** menu as shown in **Figure 6.7**. JMP chooses the statistical analysis appropriate for a variable's modeling type and its role assignment.

Figure 6.7 Select the Fit Y by X Analyze Command

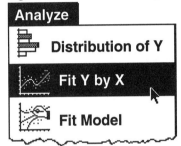

Note➡ **Fit Y by X** does the following kinds of analyses:

- categorical analysis when both X and Y have nominal or ordinal values, as in this example
- analysis of variance when X is nominal and Y has continuous values
- logistic regression when X is continuous and Y has nominal or ordinal values
- regression analysis when both X and Y have nominal values, as in this example.

Assign Variable Roles

In this investigation, the country, size, and type columns are dependent response (Y) variables. Sex, marital status, and age(50%) are independent (X) variables.

You can choose variable roles by using the role assignment pop–up menu at the top of each column. Alternatively, you can select an analysis command from the **Analyze** menu and respond to a variable role dialog prompt. The market researcher responds to the role assignment dialog displayed by the **Fit Y by X** command.

8   The market researcher holds down the command key, clicks the three Y variables, and then clicks the **Y** button. The X variables are assigned in the same manner using the **X** button. The dialog in **Figure 6.8** shows the result. The market researcher clicks **Done** when the dialog is complete.

Figure 6.8 Role Assignment Dialog

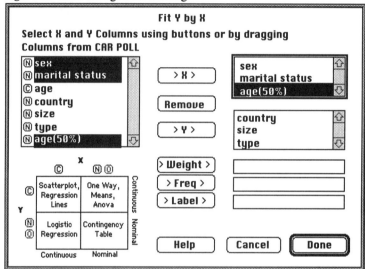

Contingency Table Mosaic Plots

If both X and Y have either nominal or ordinal values, the Fit Y by X platform displays a contingency table mosaic plot with accompanying text reports for each combination of X and Y columns. The market researcher can scroll across and down the report window to see each relationship.

A mosaic chart has side–by–side divided bars for each level of its X variable. The bars are divided into segments proportional to each discrete Y value. The mosaic chart in **Figure 6.9** shows the relationship of marital status to the manufacturing country.

The width of each bar is proportional to the sample size. When the lines dividing the bars align horizontally, the response proportions are the same. When the lines are far apart, the response rates of the samples may be statistically different.

Figure 6.9 Mosaic Bar Plot Axes

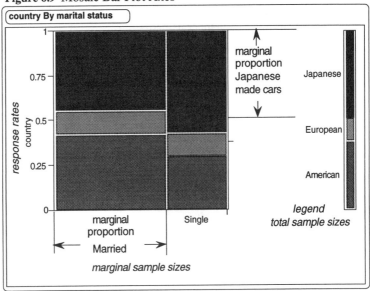

9   The researcher scrolls horizontally to see each X variable as it relates to manufacturing country.

What can be said about country?   Sex and country do not appear to have any relationship at all. The proportion of automobiles from the three manufacturing countries is about the same for each sex.

The country by age(50%) mosaic shows that the proportion of American car owners over 30 is only slightly greater than the proportion of American car owners under 30.

The most significant relationship occurs between marital status and country. The mosaic plot shown previously in **Figure 6.9** and its supporting Tests table shown in **Figure 6.10** suggest that married people are more likely than single people to own American cars.

There are statistical text tables accompanying each mosaic plot. You can open and close these reports as needed by clicking on the appropriate reveal/conceal buttons.

The Likelihood Ratio and Pearson chi–square tests in **Figure 6.10** evaluate the relationship between an automobile's country of manufacture and the marital status of owner. If no relationship exists between country and marital status, a smaller chi–square value than the one computed would occur only 7 times in 100 similar surveys.

Because of these statistical results the market researcher plans to advise the American auto manufacturer to direct some advertising plans toward married couples.

Figure 6.10 Tests Report for Country and Marital Status

Tests			
Source	DF	–LogLikelihood	RSquare (U)
Model	2	2.57004	0.0086
Error	299	295.88121	
C Total	301	298.45125	
Total Count	303		
Test	ChiSquare	Prob>ChiSq	
Likelihood Ratio	5.140	0.0765	
Pearson	5.081	0.0788	

10   Next, the market researcher scrolls down to the first mosaic plot in the second row and then scrolls across to see the relationship between size of car and each X variable.

What can be said about size of car?   The three mosaic plots in the second row show no relationship between car size and gender, marital status, or age group. The market researcher looks at Crosstabs and the Tests tables beneath each of the mosaic plots in the second row (See **Figure 6.11**).

The chi–square values support the hypothesis that the purchase of large, medium, and small cars is not significantly different across these factor levels. The chi–square probabilities range from .21 to .3, which means you expect smaller chi–square values to occur 21–30 times in 100 similar surveys.

Figure 6.11 Tables for Relationships with Size of Car

Gender and Size of Car

Crosstabs ▶

		sex		
Count	Female	Male	
Large	17	25	42
Medium	63	61	124
Small	58	79	137
	138	165	303

Tests

Source	DF	–LogLikelihood	RSquare (U)
Model	2	1.19399	0.0039
Error	299	301.33262	
C Total	301	302.52662	
Total Count	303		

Test	ChiSquare	Prob>ChiSq
Likelihood Ratio	2.388	0.3030
Pearson	2.388	0.3030

Marital Status and Size of Car

Crosstabs ▶

		marital status		
Count	Married	Single	
Large	30	12	42
Medium	84	40	124
Small	82	55	137
	196	107	303

Tests

Source	DF	–LogLikelihood	RSquare (U)
Model	2	1.37635	0.0045
Error	299	301.15026	
C Total	301	302.52662	
Total Count	303		

Test	ChiSquare	Prob>ChiSq
Likelihood Ratio	2.753	0.2525
Pearson	2.743	0.2537

Age Group and Size of Car

Crosstabs ▶

		age group		
Count	0	1	
Large	27	15	42
Medium	65	59	124
Small	67	70	137
	159	144	303

Tests

Source	DF	–LogLikelihood	RSquare (U)
Model	2	1.54503	0.0051
Error	299	300.98158	
C Total	301	302.52662	
Total Count	303		

Test	ChiSquare	Prob>ChiSq
Likelihood Ratio	3.090	0.2133
Pearson	3.049	0.2177

The market researcher can tell the American automobile manufacturer that it makes no difference what size cars show in advertisements.

11   The market survey categorizes cars based on both size and type, where a car's type is go–to–work, sporty, or family. The market researcher scrolls across the third row of plots to look at the relationship between type of car and each of these X variables.

What can be said about type of car?

The mosaic plots in **Figures 6.12** and **6.13** show that type of car varies for levels of marital status and age class. As you might expect, many of the cars owned by married people are family automobiles, while the largest proportion of cars owned by single people are sporty cars.

Figure 6.12 Reports for Type of Car and Marital Status

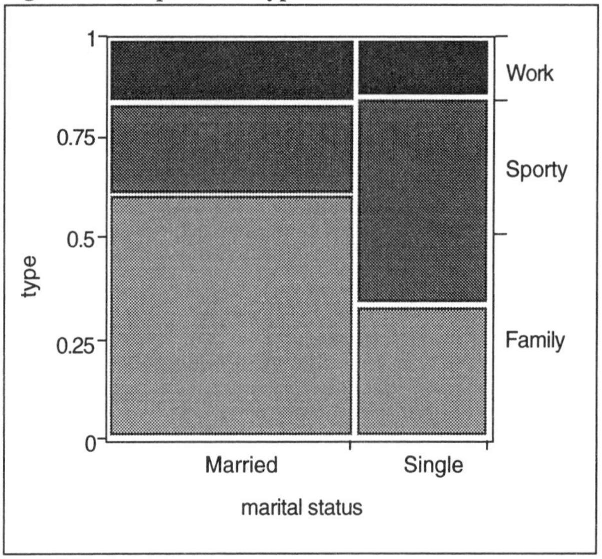

Tests			
Source	DF	–LogLikelihood	RSquare (U)
Model	2	13.38280	0.0441
Error	299	289.81268	
C Total	301	303.19548	
Total Count	303		

Test	ChiSquare	Prob>ChiSq
Likelihood Ratio	26.766	0.0000
Pearson	26.963	0.0000

The market researcher plans to advise the American automobile manufacturer to emphasize married couples buying family–type automobiles when advertising.

It follows logically that a relationship between age group and type of car also exists because older people are more likely to be married. **Figure 6.13** shows graphically that the proportion of people over 30 years old who own family cars is much greater than those under 30.

The small chi–square values support the significant difference in proportions. The chi–square values of .0003 mean that you expect proportions as varied as these to occur only 3 times in 1,000 similar surveys.

Figure 6.13 Reports for Type of Car and Age Group

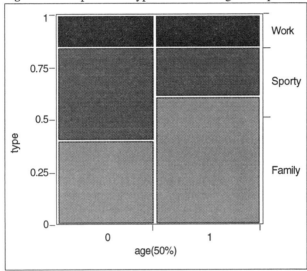

Test	ChiSquare	Prob>ChiSq
Likelihood Ratio	16.098	0.0003
Pearson	15.953	0.0003

Chapter Summary

In this chapter a market researcher looked at relationships between categorical variables obtained from a survey. The survey recorded age, sex, marital status, and information about the type of automobile owned by a random sample of people in the same geographical area. The auto information included manufacturing country, size, and type of car. Car types were classified as go–to–work, sporty, and family. The market researcher investigated the question,

"Is the size of car, type of car, or manufacturing country related to the age, gender, or marital status of the owner? "

The **Fit Y by X** command produced nine mosaic charts with supporting statistical summaries that show

- no relationship between either sex or age and manufacturing country
- a significant relationship between marital status and manufacturing country with married people more likely to own American cars than single people
- no relationship between sex, age, or marital status and size of car
- no relationship between sex and type of car
- significant relationships between marital status and type of car. As might be expected, married people over 30 years old were more likely to own family type cars than younger, single people.

The market researcher prepared a final report to the American automobile manufacturer. The report recommended that the advertising campaign focus toward married couples who appear to be over 30 years old looking for a family car.

Chapter 5, "Contingency Tables," in the *JMP Statistics and Graphics Guide* discusses analyzing categorical data in more detail.

For more information about the calculator, see Chapter 5, "Calculator Functions," and Chapter 6, "Using the Calculator," in the *JMP User's Guide*.

Chapter 7
Regression and Curve Fitting

Class Assignment

A statistics professor has given an exploratory regression assignment to a class. The assignment is to select a set of data suitable for regression analysis and to compare various regression model fits. One student knows about the interactive regression capabilities of JMP and is eager to start the class project.

The student chooses data from Eppright *et al.* (1972) as reported in Eubank (1988, p. 272). The study subjects are young males. The variables in the data table are age (in months) and the ratio of weight to height. A third variable classifies the subjects into two groups based on age. The student's goal is to describe and model the growth pattern of subjects for the age range given in the data table.

Look Before You Leap

The first step is to become familiar with the data. The student begins by reviewing the data to determine the best way to proceed with the regression assignment.

Open a JMP File

1 The student double–clicks the JMP application to begin, and opens the GROWTH file in the SAMPLE DATA folder (growth.jmp under Windows). Alternatively, if you double–click the JMP file, JMP begins automatically. The GROWTH (or GROWTH.JMP) data table appears in spreadsheet form as shown in **Figure 7.1**.

Figure 7.1 The GROWTH Data Table

GROWTH.JMP		
2 Cols	C □	C □
72 Rows	ratio	age
1	0.46	0.5
2	0.47	1.5
3	0.56	2.5
4	0.61	3.5

GROWTH.JMP		
2 Cols	C □	C □
72 Rows	ratio	age
70	1.01	69.5
71	0.99	70.5
72	1.04	71.5

As shown in **Figure 7.1**, the student sees there are 2 columns and 72 rows. The ratio column contains the average weight/height ratio for each age group in the study. The age groups range from .5 to 71.5 months, as illustrated in **Figure 7.1**.

The *modeling type* for each column shows in the modeling type box above the column name. Both columns have *continuous* modeling types (C), as needed for the regression assignment.

Choose Variable Roles

2 To continue with the regression and curve fitting assignment, the student chooses a role assignment for each variable as shown in **Figure 7.2**. The role assignment box at the top of each column accesses a pop–up menu that the student uses to assign the role of **X** for age and **Y** for ratio.

- **Y** identifies a response or dependent variable.
- **X** identifies a classification or independent variable.

Figure 7.2 Assign Variable Roles to ratio and age

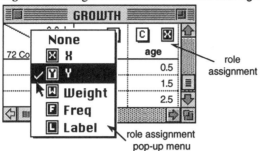

Note➜ If you do not assign variable roles in the spreadsheet, a dialog prompts you to assign roles when you select a command from the **Analyze** menu.

Select an Analysis Platform

The student's next step is to choose a command from the **Analyze** menu that fits regression curves to continuous data. JMP then completes the statistical analysis appropriate for the column role assignments, each variable's modeling type, and the analysis platform.

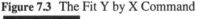 3 To fit regression curves, the student selects the **Fit Y by X** command from the **Analyze** menu.

Figure 7.3 The Fit Y by X Command

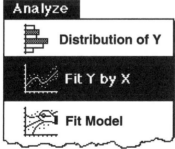

Note➡ **Fit Y by X** automatically does four kinds of analyses:

- categorical analysis when both **X** and **Y** have nominal or ordinal values
- analysis of variance when **X** is nominal and **Y** has continuous values
- logistic regression when **X** is continuous and **Y** has nominal or ordinal values
- regression analysis when both **X** and **Y** have continuous values, as in this example.

When both the X and Y variables have continuous values, the Fit Y by X platform displays a scatterplot of the values as shown in **Figure 7.4**.

Figure 7.4 Scatterplot of Ratio by Age

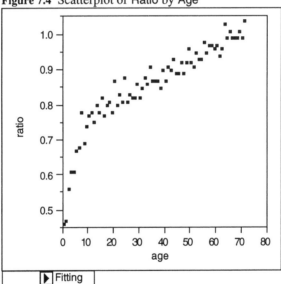

How do the data points look? The student sees at a glance that the growth pattern is not random and decides that a straight line regression is a good baseline fit to compare with other regression curves.

Fitting Models to Continuous Data

The Fitting menu, shown in **Figure 7.5**, lists a **Show Points** toggle command and five commands for regression fits.

Figure 7.5 Regression Fitting Pop–up Menu

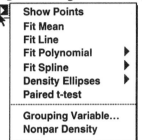

Note➡ The fitting commands are not toggles. You can select them repeatedly, which means that the student can overlay different fits on the same plot to compare them.

The Fit Line Command

The student first selects **Fit Line** from the Fitting pop–up menu to fit a simple regression line through the data points (**Figure 7.6**). The regression line minimizes the sum of squared distances from each point to the line of fit. The Linear Fit pop–up menu lets you show confidence curves, save predicted and residual values as new data table columns, or remove the fit from the plot. The **Save Predicteds** command also saves the prediction equation for the fit with the column of predicted values.

Figure 7.6 Linear fit of Ratio by Age

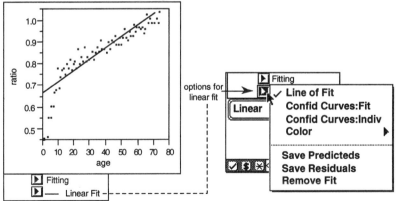

5   The regression line appears to fit the growth data fairly well. However, the student wants to evaluate the linear fit with statistical text reports. To follow along with the student, click the **Linear Fit** reveal button beneath the scatterplot. Three more reveal buttons appear, each corresponding to a different statistical report. Note that the first two reports are already open. For expediency, the **Reveal All** command in the asterisk pop–up menu to the left of the horizontal scroll bar opens all reports at once.

Figure 7.7 Text Report Reveal Buttons for Regression

The Summary of Fit Table

6   The Summary of Fit table, shown in **Figure 7.8**, is a numeric summary of the linear fit.

Figure 7.8 Summary of Fit Table for Linear Regression

Summary of Fit	
RSquare	0.822535
RSquare Adj	0.819999
Root Mean Square Error	0.051653
Mean of Response	0.855556
Observations (or Sum Wgts)	72

The following list describes the items in the Summary of Fit table:

*   Rsquare quantifies the proportion of total variation in the growth ratios accounted for by fitting the regression line.
*   Rsquare Adj adjusts Rsquare to make it more comparable over models with different numbers of parameters.
*   Root Mean Square Error (RMSE) is a measure of the variation in the ratio values that is attributable to different people rather than to different ages.
*   Mean of Response is the mean (arithmetic average) of the ratio values.
*   Observations is the total number of nonmissing values.

The Analysis of Variance Table

7 Next, the student reviews the Analysis of Variance table shown in **Figure 7.9**.

Figure 7.9 Analysis of Variance Table for Linear Regression

Analysis of Variance				
Source	**DF**	**Sum of Squares**	**Mean Square**	**F Ratio**
Model	1	0.8656172	0.865617	324.4433
Error	70	0.1867605	0.002668	**Prob > F**
C. Total	71	1.0523778		0.0000

The following list describes the items in the Analysis of Variance table:

- **Source** identifies the sources of variation in the growth ratio values (Model, Error, and C. Total).
- **DF** records the associated degrees of freedom for each source of variation.
- **Sum of Squares** (SS for short) quantifies the variation associated with each source of variation. The C Total SS is the corrected total SS computed from all the ratio values. It divides (partitions) into the SS for Model and SS for Error.

  The model SS is the amount of the total variation in the ratio scores explained by fitting a straight line to the data.

  The error SS is the remaining or unexplained variation.
- **Mean Square** lists the Sum of Squares divided by its associated degrees of freedom (**DF**) for Model and Error.
- The **F Ratio** is the regression (Model) mean square divided by the Error mean square.
- **Prob > F** is the probability of a greater F value occurring if the ratio values differed only because of different subjects rather than because the subjects are different ages.

In this example the significance of the F value is .0000, which strongly indicates that the linear fit to the weight/height growth pattern is significantly better than the horizontal line that fits the sample mean to the data.

The Parameter Estimates Table

8 The student now clicks the **Parameter Estimates** reveal button to open the remaining table shown in **Figure 7.10**. The following list describes the items in the Parameter Estimates table:

- **Term** lists the parameter terms in the regression model.
- **Estimate** lists the estimates of the coefficients in the regression line equation.
- **Std Error** lists estimates of the standard error of the parameters.
- **t Ratio** is the parameter estimate divided by its standard error.
- **Prob > |t|** is the probability of a greater absolute t value occurring by chance alone if the parameter has no effect in the model.

Figure 7.10 Parameter Estimates Table for Linear Regression

Parameter Estimates

Term	Estimate	Std Error	t Ratio	Prob>|t|
Intercept	0.6656231	0.01218	54.67	0.0000
age	0.0052759	0.00029	18.01	0.0000

How well does the line fit the data? The significant F ratio in the Analysis of Variance table tells the student that the regression line fits significantly better than the horizontal line at the mean (the simple mean model). However, while the regression line looks like a good fit for age groups above 7 months, it does not describe the data well for ages younger than 7 months.

The Exclude Command

Since the low–age points are the trouble spots for the linear fit, the student decides to remove them from the analysis and to try the model with the remaining values. To highlight these outliers and exclude them from the analysis, the student

9
·
·
12

- selects the brush tool from the **Tools** menu
- shift–drags the brush over the points to be excluded
- uses the **Exclude** command from the **Rows** menu to mark the points as excluded
- uses the **Markers** command from the **Rows** menu to assign the **x** marker to the excluded points.

You can follow these steps and then choose the **Fit Line** command again to see the results of excluding the low–age points. **Figure 7.11** shows both regression lines. The low–age points still show on the plot but are not included in the second regression line's computation.

Figure 7.11 Linear Fit with Outliers Excluded

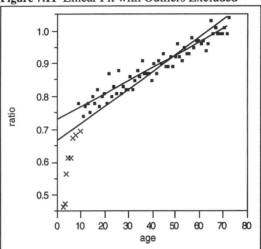

13   After completing this part of the exploratory regression analysis, the student selects the arrow tool and chooses **Journal** from the **Edit** menu.

The first time the **Journal** command is selected during a JMP session, a journal window opens and fills with the graphs and tables from the report window. Then, the Save command displays the dialog shown in **Figure 7.12**. The student names the journal and chooses a word processor format. A journal window opens and fills with the graphs and tables from the report window.

Figure 7.12 Journal File Save Dialog

Journaling
JMP results

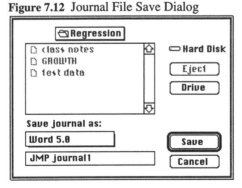

The Fit Polynomial Command

The student sees the full potential of using JMP for comparative exploratory analysis and continues by choosing a polynomial fit for comparison to the linear fit. A linear regression is simply a polynomial of degree 1. Click the Fit Y by X window for Growth to activate it. Then select the **Fit Polynomial** command and choose degrees greater than 1, allowing the fit to have curvature.

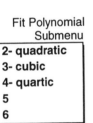

14

The student again includes all rows in the analysis. To follow along with the student,

• choose **Select Excluded** from the **Rows** menu. This highlights all currently excluded rows.

• choose the **Exclude/Include** toggle from the **Rows** menu.

15

The student also removes the line of fit that excluded the lower age groups. The **Remove Fit** option from the *second* (modified) regression line removes this line so that only the line fit to all the data points remains. See **Figure 7.6** for an illustration of the pop–up menu that accompanies each fit.

The student uses the Fitting menu twice more to overlay polynomial curves of degree 2 and degree 3 on the scatterplot. The **Polynomial** command submenu (shown to the left of **Figure 7.13**) lists the choice of degrees 2 through 6.

17

Figure 7.13 Comparison of Polynomial Fits

Fit Polynomial
Submenu

2- quadratic
3- cubic
4- quartic
5
6

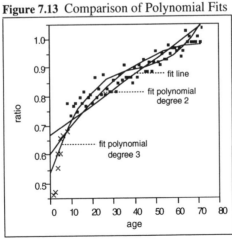

How much improvement is there? **Figure 7.14** shows a partial display of the Summary of Fit tables for the linear fit and each of the polynomial fits. As polynomial terms are added to the model, the regression curve appears to fit the data better and the Rsquare value increases.

Figure 7.14 Tables for Linear and Polynomial Fits

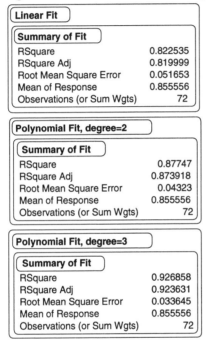

Linear Fit	
Summary of Fit	
RSquare	0.822535
RSquare Adj	0.819999
Root Mean Square Error	0.051653
Mean of Response	0.855556
Observations (or Sum Wgts)	72

Polynomial Fit, degree=2	
Summary of Fit	
RSquare	0.87747
RSquare Adj	0.873918
Root Mean Square Error	0.04323
Mean of Response	0.855556
Observations (or Sum Wgts)	72

Polynomial Fit, degree=3	
Summary of Fit	
RSquare	0.926858
RSquare Adj	0.923631
Root Mean Square Error	0.033645
Mean of Response	0.855556
Observations (or Sum Wgts)	72

In preparation for writing a report to complete the class assignment, the student also journals these results. The **Journal** command appends these results to the open journal file.

The Fit Spline Command

Even the polynomial fit of degree 3 does not quite reach the outlying points of the very young subjects. The student needs a free–form function that acts as if it smoothes the data. To do this, the **Fit Spline** command fits a *smoothing spline*.

18 The student uses the **Remove Fit** options on both polynomial fits, which leaves only the linear regression line. See **Figure 7.6** for an illustration of the pop–up menu that includes this option. Next, the student uses the Fitting menu and chooses three splines with lambda values of 10, 1,000, and 100,000. Lambda is a tuning factor that determines the flexibility of the spline. The **Fit Spline** command submenu (shown to the left of **Figure 7.15**) lists lambda values. The three new fits are overlaid on the scatterplot.

Figure 7.15 Comparison of Spline and Linear fits

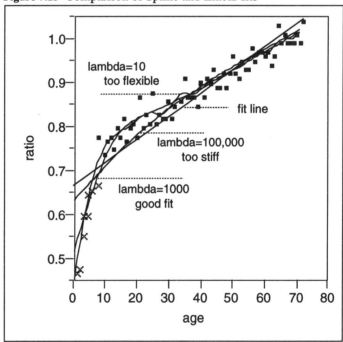

How well do the splines model the data? By inspecting the plot, the student sees that the lambda = 10 curve is too flexible and therefore local error has too great an effect on it. The lambda = 100000 curve is too stiff. It is so straight that it does not reach down to model the lower ages closely. However, the lambda = 1000 curve fits well. Its shape is not influenced by local errors, and it appears to fit the data smoothly.

Figure 7.16 Summary of Fit Tables for Spline Fits

Smoothing Spline Fit, lambda=10	
R–Square	0.970061
Sum of Squares Error	0.031508

Smoothing Spline Fit, lambda=1000	
R–Square	0.952519
Sum of Squares Error	0.049968

Smoothing Spline Fit, lambda=100000	
R–Square	0.871034
Sum of Squares Error	0.135721

The student again uses the **Journal** command from the **Edit** menu to append this scatterplot and the smoothing spine text reports to the open journal file. After journaling the final analyses, the student types the following draft notes about the spline–fitting technique at the bottom of the journal window:

```
"This fitting technique applies a cubic
polynomial to the interval between points;
the polynomial is joined such that the curve
meets at the same point with the same slope
to form a continuous and smooth curve. A
small enough lambda could make such a curve
go through every point, which would model the
error, not the mean. A moderate lambda value
forces the curve to be smoother, i.e, less
curved. This is accomplished by adding a
curvature penalty to the optimization that
minimizes the sum of squares error."
```

The regression exploration is done and the student captures the graphs and text reports in a journal file. The journal file is ready for editing to complete the class assignment.

What can the student conclude about growth rate? By comparing various regression fits, the student sees that both the polynomial fits and the spline fit with moderate flexibility best describe the data. These models show that infants grow most rapidly during the first months of life and that growth rate decreases significantly at approximately 12 months.

Extra Credit: Fitting By Groups

The professor gives extra credit for extra effort. In pursuit of upwardly mobile grades, the student mouses around in JMP and finds a convenient way to show a comparison of growth rates for groups of children. The section, **The Exclude Command**, in this chapter shows how to overlay a linear fit for the whole sample with a linear fit for children over the age of one year. The student carries this idea one step further with overlay fits to compare children under the age of 1 year with children over 1 year.

19 The student creates a new column called **stage** to act as a grouping variable. The calculator formula shown below assigns the value "babies" to each child less than 12.5 months old, and "toddlers" to children who are 12.5 months or older.

$$\begin{cases} \text{"babies"}, & \text{if } age < 12.5 \\ \text{"toddlers"}, & \text{otherwise} \end{cases}$$

The student also assigns each group a marker as shown in **Figure 7.17**.

Figure 7.17 Computed Age Grouping Variable

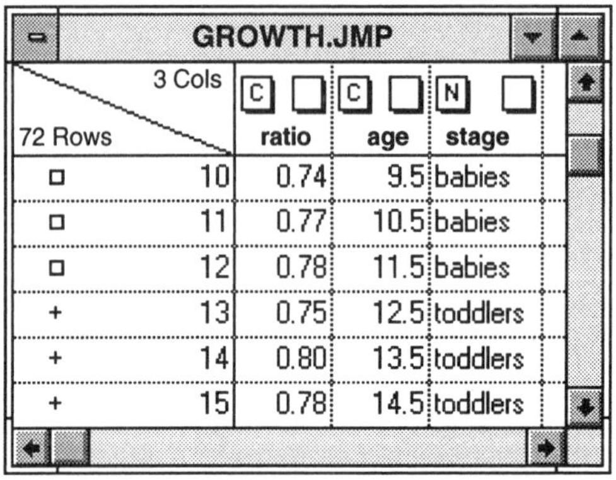
GROWTH.JMP

3 Cols / 72 Rows		ratio	age	stage
□	10	0.74	9.5	babies
□	11	0.77	10.5	babies
□	12	0.78	11.5	babies
+	13	0.75	12.5	toddlers
+	14	0.80	13.5	toddlers
+	15	0.78	14.5	toddlers

20 The **Grouping Variable** command in the Fitting pop–up menu beneath the plot displays the dialog to the right in **Figure 7.18**. The student selects **Stage**, the newly created grouping variable.

Figure 7.18 Grouping Variable Selection

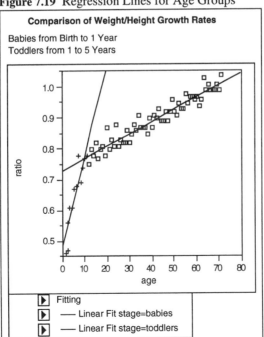

The student clears any previous fits still showing, such as those seen in **Figure 7.13**, using each fit's **Remove Fit** command.

21 Finally, the student chooses the **Fit Line** command with a grouping variable in effect, which automatically produces the overlaid regression lines shown in **Figure 7.19**. The highlighted points with markers that correspond to each regression give a dramatic visualization of the steep growth rate for babies during the first year of life compared to the more moderate growth rate of toddlers and small children aged 1 to 5 years.

Figure 7.19 Regression Lines for Age Groups

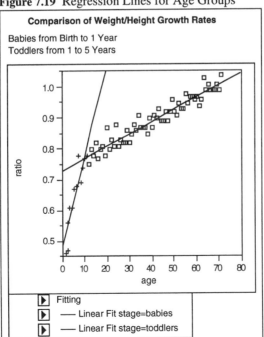

Chapter Summary

To complete a regression assignment for a statistics class, a student used the Fit Y by X analysis platform in JMP to examine a variety of regression model fits. The assignment was to model and describe the growth pattern of subjects over a range of ages. Growth was measured by the ratio of weight to height. For this assignment, the student

- fit a straight line to use as a baseline comparison to other regression models and evaluated the fit using statistical text reports
- excluded outliers and again fit a straight line to compare the Rsquare values given by the Summary of Fit tables for both lines
- fit 2nd and 3rd degree polynomials to see if they modeled the growth pattern more realistically
- fit smoothing splines with lambda values of 10, 1,000, and 100,000 and compared them with each other and with the linear fit
- used the grouping facility in the Fitting menu to compare growth rates of babies under the age of 1 year with toddlers from age 1 to 5 years.

The student used the journaling feature to append each of these regression reports and graphs to a journal file. This journal file provides the information needed to complete the class assignment on exploratory regression analysis.

See Chapter 3, "Simple Regression and Curve Fitting," in the *JMP Statistics and Graphics Guide* for a complete discussion of the regression platform.

Chapter 8
A Factorial Analysis

Popcorn yield experiment

A food manufacturer wants to offer the public two qualities of popcorn. The plain, everyday type has been serving the public for years, but now the company's research department claims to have discovered a special treatment of corn kernels. This new process supposedly increases the popcorn yield as measured by popcorn volume from a given measure of kernels.

Corporate decision makers want to know if this is really true and, if so, how much the yield increases. Because special treatment raises the cost of the popcorn, the increase in yield must be significant enough to cover the higher processing costs.

Decisions must also be made about packaging, cost, and advertising for the new corn. The decision makers want to know if the increased yield (if indeed there really is one) is the same under all popping conditions or better under some than others.

(The popcorn data used in this chapter and for examples in the *JMP User's Guide* and the *JMP Statistics and Graphics Guide* are artificial, but the experiment was inspired by experimental data reported in Box, Hunter, and Hunter (1978).)

Look Before You Leap

The popcorn yield data are the result of a designed experiment. The same amounts of different kinds of corn were methodically popped under different conditions. A scientist from the research department first looks at the data to review the results of the popcorn experiment.

Open a Data Table

The popcorn research data are in a JMP file called POPCORN in the SAMPLE DATA folder on the Macintosh (popcorn.jmp in the data folder under Windows). The research scientist double–clicks the POPCORN file to begin a JMP session. The POPCORN data table displays in spreadsheet form. A partial listing of the table is shown in **Figure 8.1**.

Figure 8.1 The POPCORN Data Table

POPCORN				
popcorn	**oil amt**	**batch**	**yield**	**trial**
5 plain	little	small	9.9	1
6 gourmet	little	small	12.1	1
7 plain	lots	small	10.6	1
8 gourmet	lots	small	18.0	1
9 plain	little	large	8.8	2
10 gourmet	little	large	8.2	2
11 plain	lots	large	8.8	2
12 gourmet	lots	large	9.8	2

5 Cols, 16 Rows

For the experiment, the scientist popped corn under controlled conditions. Plain popcorn and specially treated gourmet popcorn were each popped in large or small amounts of oil and in large or small batches. Two trials were done for both kinds of corn under all popping conditions.

This experimental design is called a factorial design. The experiment has three factors, usually called *main effects*, which are

- kind of popcorn (plain or gourmet)
- amount of cooking oil (little or lots)
- cooking batch size (large or small).

What Questions Can Be Asked?

The appropriate statistical analysis for a factorial design addresses the following questions about the main effects:

- Is there an overall difference in yield between plain and gourmet popcorn?
- Is there an overall difference in yield between cooking in lots of oil instead of a small amount of oil?
- What is the difference in yield between cooking several small batches instead of one large batch?

Analysis of a factorial experiment also provides information about the *interaction* between the main effects as addressed by the following questions:

- Does the amount of cooking oil have the same effect on both types of popcorn? In other words, is there an interaction effect between popcorn type and amount of cooking oil used?
- Is there an interaction effect between cooking batch size and type of popcorn?
- Is there an interaction effect between batch size and amount of oil used?
- Are there interaction effects among the three main effects?

The Fit Model Dialog

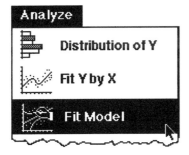

Next, select **Fit Model** in the **Analyze** menu as shown to the left.

The **Fit Model** command lets you specify and analyze complex models like the factorial design described in the previous section.

In this example, the columns do not have X and Y roles assigned in the spreadsheet. Instead, the **Fit Model** command displays the dialog shown in **Figure 8.2**. The scientist uses the dialog to designate the type of model, the model response variables, and the effects in the model.

To specify the factorial model, the scientist

3

- selects (use COMMAND–click on the Macintosh and CONTROL–click under Windows) popcorn, oil amt, and batch from the column selector list

- selects **Full factorial** from the Effect Macros pop–up menu

6

- selects yield from the column selector list as shown in **Figure 8.2**

- clicks the Y response button.

Figure 8.2 The Fit Model Dialog

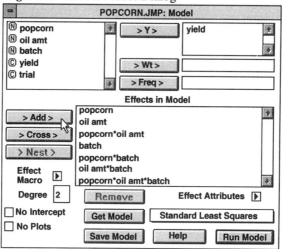

The **Factorial** button adds all main effects and interactions (*crossed effects*) to the **Effects in Model** window. When the need arises, the scientist can tailor the model further by adding effects or removing unwanted effects with the **Add** and **Remove** buttons.

7 When the Fit Model dialog is complete, the scientist clicks **Run Model** to estimate the model parameters and view the results.

Graphical Display: Leverage Plots

The Fit Model platform graphically displays the whole model and each model effect as the *leverage plots* shown in **Figures 8.3** through **8.6**. The scientist can tell at a glance whether the factorial model explains the popcorn data, and which factors are most influential.

What can be said about the Factorial model?

...the type of popcorn?

The Whole–model plot to the left in **Figure 8.3** shows actual yield and predicted yield values with a regression line and 95% confidence curves. The plot to the right is a yield by popcorn leverage plot. In both displays the regression line and the 95% confidence curves cross the sample mean (the horizontal line).

These two plots tell the scientist that the whole factorial model) all effects together) explains a significant proportion of the variation in popcorn yield. There is also a significance difference in yield between the two types of popcorn.

Figure 8.3 Leverage Plots for the Whole Model and popcorn Effects

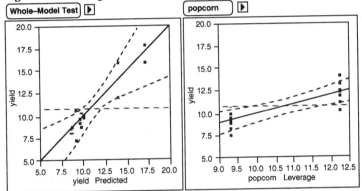

What can be said about oil amt and popcorn?

The confidence curves for oil amt and the popcorn*oil amt interaction do not cross the horizontal mean line. This tells the scientist that neither of these factors is a significant effect in the experiment.

Figure 8.4 Leverage Plots for the oil amt and the Interaction Effects

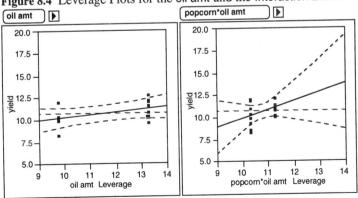

What can be said about batch size?

...about interaction between popcorn and batch size?

The leverage plots in **Figure 8.5** show that the batch effect (batch) and the interaction between popcorn type and batch size (popcorn*batch) are significant effects. This means that the size of the batch makes a difference in the popcorn yield. Furthermore, the significant interaction means that batch size affects each type of popcorn differently.

Figure 8.5 Leverage Plots for the batch and Interaction Effects

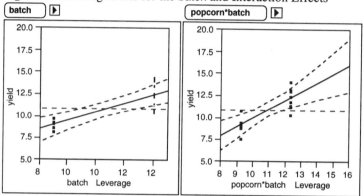

What can be said about the other interactions?

The two leverage plots shown in **Figure 8.6** show that there is no significant interaction between amount of oil and batch size, and there is no *three–way* interaction between the model main effects

Figure 8.6 Leverage Plots for Interaction Effects

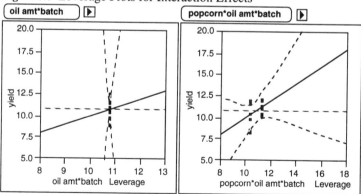

For more information about interpretation of leverage plots, see Chapter 1, "Understanding JMP Analyses," Chapter 8, "Standard Least Squares Model Fitting," and "Appendix A" in the *JMP Statistics and Graphics Guide*.

Quantify Results: Statistical Reports

Because oil amt and its interactions with other effects are insignificant, the scientist fits the popcorn data again without these effects. The new model has the significant factors, type of popcorn, batch size, and their interaction term. This approach condenses the statistical reports that show estimates of yield under the different conditions of interest.

8   The scientist uses the same Fit Model dialog window as before. If you closed the Fit Model dialog used previously, select **Fit Model** from the **Analyze** menu again to open a new model dialog. Use any of the following methods to specify the two–factor model:

- From the full factorial model, select unwanted effects listed in the **Effects in Model** box and click **Remove**.
- Remove all effects for the previous model. Then COMMAND–click (CONTROL–click under Windows) to select only the **popcorn** and **batch** columns in the column selector list. Select **Full Factorial** in the **Effects Macro** pop–up menu.
- Remove all effects for the previous model, select **popcorn** and **batch** from the column selector list and click **Add**. Then COMMAND–click (CONTROL–click under Windows) to select them again in the column list, and click **Cross** as shown in **Figure 8.7**.

Figure 8.7 Specify an Interaction Term

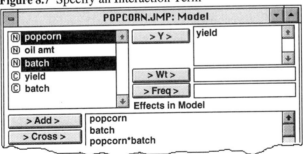

Analysis of Variance

9   When the scientist clicks **Run Model**, the leverage plots for the reduced model open. The whole model leverage plot, shown in **Figure 8.8**, shows that the two–factor model describes the popcorn experiment well. The scientist examines the tables that accompany the whole–model leverage plot.

The Analysis of Variance table, beneath the whole–model leverage plot, quantifies the analysis results. It lists the *partitioning* of the total variation of the sample into components. The ratio of the Mean Square components forms an F statistic that evaluates the effectiveness of the model fit. If the probability associated with the F ratio is small, then the analysis of variance model fits better statistically than the simple model that contains only the overall response mean.

Figure 8.8 Analysis of Variance for the Two–Factor Whole Model

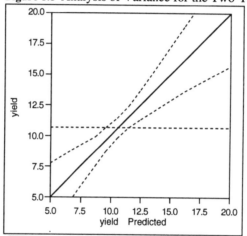

Analysis of Variance

Source	DF	Sum of Squares	Mean Square	F Ratio
Model	3	121.02000	40.3400	16.9853
Error	12	28.50000	2.3750	**Prob > F**
C Total	15	149.52000		0.0001

The following list describes the Analysis of Variance table:

- **Source** identifies the sources of variation in the growth ratio values (Model, Error, and C. Total).
- **DF** records the degrees of freedom for each source of variation.
- **Sum of Squares** (SS for short) quantifies the variation in yield. C Total is the corrected total SS. It is divided (partitioned) into the SS for Model and SS for Error.

  The SS for Model is the variation in the yield explained by the analysis of variance model, which hypothesizes that the model factors have a significant effect.

  The SS for Error is the remaining or unexplained variation.
- A **Mean Square** is a sum of squares divided by its associated degrees of freedom (**DF**).

- The **F ratio** is the model mean square divided by the error mean square.
- **Prob > F** is the probability of a greater F value occurring if the variation in popcorn yield resulted from chance alone rather than from the model effects.

In this example, the significance of the F value is .0001. This implies that the difference found in the popcorn yield produced by this experiment is expected only 1 time in 10,000 similar trials if the model factors do not affect the popcorn yield.

Model Summary Reports

10 The reveal buttons to the left of the leverage plots provide the scientist with statistical summaries (**Figure 8.9**). The Summary of Fit table shows the numeric summaries of the response for the factorial model:

- The **Rsquare** of .809 tells the scientist that the two–factor model explains nearly 81% of the variation in the data.
- **Rsquare Adj** adjusts **Rsquare** to make it more comparable over models with different numbers of parameters.
- **Root Mean Square Error (RMSE)** is a measure of the variation in the yield scores that can be attributed to random error rather than differences in the model's factors.
- **Mean of Response** is the mean (average) of the yield scores.
- **Observations** is the total number of recorded scores.

The F–test probabilities in the Effect Test table tell the scientist that all model factors explain a significant proportion of the total variation.

Figure 8.9 Summary Tables for the Two–Factor Model Response

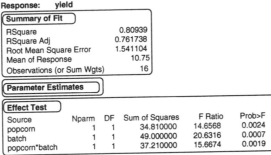

Response: yield

Summary of Fit

RSquare	0.80939
RSquare Adj	0.761738
Root Mean Square Error	1.541104
Mean of Response	10.75
Observations (or Sum Wgts)	16

Parameter Estimates

Effect Test

Source	Nparm	DF	Sum of Squares	F Ratio	Prob>F
popcorn	1	1	34.810000	14.6568	0.0024
batch	1	1	49.000000	20.6316	0.0007
popcorn*batch	1	1	37.210000	15.6674	0.0019

There are also additional tables showing beneath the leverage plots for each effect in the model.

Factor Summary Reports

11   The scientist now looks below the leverage plots to see the summary tables for each effect in the model. The tables for the main effects are shown in **Figure 8.10** and **8.11**. The Least Squares Means table lists the least squares means and standard errors for each level of the model factors, without considering the interaction between them. In this balanced example, the least squares means are simply the sample means of each factor level.

Figure 8.10 Tables for the popcorn Effect

Effect Test

Sum of Squares	F Ratio	DF	Prob>F
34.810000	14.6568	1	0.0024

Least Squares Means

Level	Least Sq Mean	Std Error	Mean
gourmet	12.22500000	0.5448623679	12.2250
plain	9.27500000	0.5448623679	9.2750

Figure 8.11 Tables for the batch size Effect

Effect Test

Sum of Squares	F Ratio	DF	Prob>F
49.000000	20.6316	1	0.0007

Least Squares Means

Level	Least Sq Mean	Std Error	Mean
large	9.00000000	0.5448623679	9.0000
small	12.50000000	0.5448623679	12.5000

12   The nature of the interaction is important in the interpretation of the popcorn experiment. To examine the significant popcorn*batch interaction, the scientist selects the **Plot Effect** option from the pop–up menu next to the effect name. This option plots the least squares means for each combination of effect levels, as shown in **Figure 8.12**.

Figure 8.12 Profile Plot for the Interaction Effect

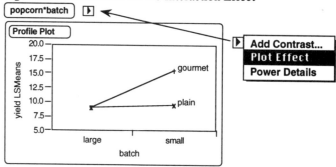

The tables below the profile plot (**Figure 8.13**) for the popcorn*batch effect tell the whole story. Batch size makes no difference for the plain brand popcorn, but popping in small batches increases the yield in the new gourmet brand.

Figure 8.13 Tables for the Interaction Effect

Effect Test

Sum of Squares	F Ratio	DF	Prob>F
37.210000	15.6674	1	0.0019

Least Squares Means

Level	Least Sq Mean	Std Error
gourmet,large	8.95000000	0.7705517504
gourmet,small	15.50000000	0.7705517504
plain,large	9.05000000	0.7705517504
plain,small	9. 50000000	0.7705517504

13 Because the factorial model with two–factors is a good prediction model, the scientist selects the **Save Prediction Formula** command from the save ($) pop–up menu. The save ($) menu is on the lower left of the horizontal scroll bar. This command creates a new column in the POPCORN data table called Pred Formula yield that contains the predicted values for each experimental condition.

The prediction formula shown in **Figure 8.14** becomes part of the column information. The scientist selects the **Column info** command for the new column and clicks on the formula box in the dialog. The prediction formula shows in a calculator window. A description of the experiment, a summary of the analysis, and the this prediction formula copied from the calculator form the basis of a report to the corporate decision makers.

Figure 8.14 Prediction Formula for Popcorn Yield

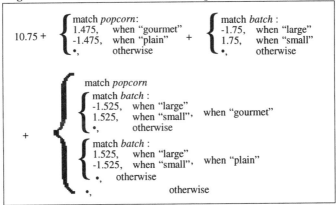

What can
the scientist
conclude?

In the report to the corporate decision makers, the scientist intends to advise that the new gourmet popcorn be placed on the market

- in small packages so that the yield will be good
- in family size packages with smaller packets inside
- in family size packages with popping instructions that clearly state the best batch size for good results.

Chapter Summary

In this chapter, a food research scientist performed a designed experiment to evaluate the difference in yield between two types of popcorn. A three–factor factorial experimental design was the basis for popcorn popping trials. The scientist analyzed the results by using the **Fit Model** command and found the following results:

- The leverage plots for the factorial analysis of three factors showed one main effect and its associated interactions to be insignificant.
- A more compact two–factor analysis with interaction adequately described the variation in yield for the popcorn trials.
- The interaction between the two main effects was significant. The Least Squares Means table for the interaction showed how the two types of popcorn behaved under different popping conditions.

The scientist concluded that the new, more expensive gourmet popcorn had better yield than the plain everyday type only if popped in small batches. The scientist advised the corporate decision makers to market the new, more expensive type of gourmet popcorn in small packets or in larger quantities with carefully worded popping instructions.

Chapter 9
Exploring Data
Advanced Example

Exploration is the search to find something new—the endeavor to make some discovery. For data analysis, exploratory study is often the most fruitful part of the analytical process because it is the most open to serendipity. Something you notice about your data can be the seed of an important advance.

There are two important aspects of exploration:

- What is the pattern or shape of the data?
- Are there points unusually far away from the bulk of the data (*outliers*)?

When you explore data composed of many variables, the great challenge is dealing with this high dimensionality. You can have many variables that have interesting relationships, but it's hard to visualize the relationship of more than a few variables at a time.

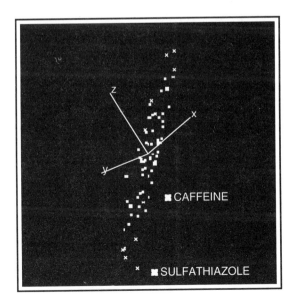

Solubility Data

A chemist interested in studying solubility is looking for compounds with unusual solubility patterns in various solvents. Data from an experiment (Koehler, Grigoras, and Dunn (1988)) are in the SOLUBILITY (solubil.jmp) file in the SAMPLE DATA folder. There are 72 compounds tested with six solvents, labeled eth, oct, cc14, c6c6, hex, and chc13. To follow the exploratory path the chemist takes, double–click the JMP file (SOLUBILITY or solubil.jmp) to begin a JMP session. Next, assign the role of Label to the column called Labels (see **Figure 9.1**) so that the names instead of row numbers identify points in plots.

Figure 9.1 The Solubility Data Table

SOLUBILITY						
7 cols	N	L	C eth	C oct	C ccl4	C c6c6	C hex	C chcl3

72 rows	Labels	eth	oct	ccl4	c6c6	hex	chcl3
47	I-VANILIN			0.04	0.74	-0.85	1.18
48	I-BUTYLALCOHOL	Assign Label Role		-0.32	-0.11	-0.60	0.34
49	PHENOBARBITOL	0.98	1.45	-0.63	-0.01	-2.22	0.62
50	PENTABARBITOL	1.28	2.10	-0.03	0.74	-1.30	1.38
51	CAFFEINE	-1.30	-0.07	-0.68	-0.16	-2.18	1.32
52	NICOTINE	1.08	1.13	0.94	0.98	0.03	1.89
53	8-QUINOLINOL	0.88	2.02	2.06	2.80	1.35	2.60

There are 6 variables but no six–dimensional graphics. However, you can look at 6 one–dimensional graphs, 15 two–dimensional graphs, and 20 three–dimensional spinning plots. Using principal components, you can even display a representation of higher dimensions.

One–Dimensional Views

The **Distribution of Y** platform summarizes data one column at a time. You don't see any relationships between variables, but the shape of the individual distributions helps you identify the one–dimensional outliers.

To begin exploring the solubility data, launch the **Distribution of Y** platform and select the six solubility columns. Their histograms, resized and trimmed of other output, are shown in **Figure 9.2**. When you click any histogram bar, that bar and all other representations of that data highlight in all related windows. In this example, click the outlying bars in each histogram to see how those values are distributed in the other histograms. Shift–click the outlying bars of each histogram to extend the selection so that it includes the outlying rows in each single dimension. You can use the **Markers** submenu in the **Rows** menu to assign x's (or any marker) to these selected rows. These markers show in the data table and in subsequent plots.

Figure 9.2 One–Dimensional Views

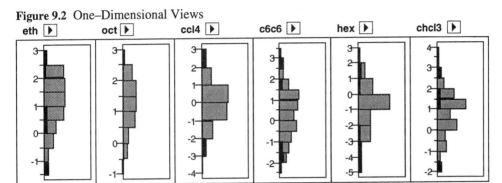

Once you highlight and mark the one–dimensional outliers, you can create a new data table containing only those rows using the **Subset** command in the **Tables** menu. Scroll through the new table as illustrated in **Figure 9.3** to see the 15 compound names selected as one–dimensional outliers.

Figure 9.3 Subset of One–Dimensional Outliers

	Labels
1	METHANOL
2	ACETIC_ACID
3	CHLOROACETIC ACID
4	ETHYLAMINE
5	2-NAPHTHOL
6	HYDROQUININE
7	P-AMINOBENZOIC ACID
8	CAFFEINE

	Labels
9	8-QUINOLINOL
10	ANISOLE
11	2-6-DIMETHYLPHENOL
12	M-CHLOROPHENOL
13	SULFATHIAZOLE
14	BENZOYLACETONE
15	O-METHOXYBENZOIC ACID

Two–Dimensional Views

You can use the **Correlation of Y's** command to display a matrix of all 30 two–dimensional scatterplots, as shown in **Figure 9.4**. The one–dimensional outliers appear as x's in each scatterplot.

Figure 9.4 Two–Dimensional View

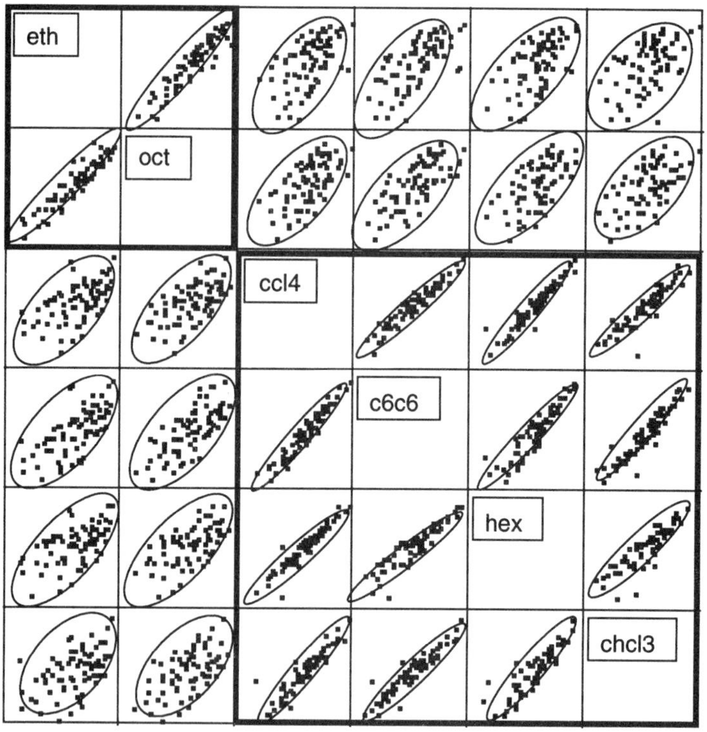

Note that many of the variables appear to be correlated in the above matrix, as evidenced by the diagonal flattening of the normal bivariate density ellipses. There appear to be two groups of variables that correlate among themselves but are not very correlated with variables in the other group.

The variables eth and oct appear to make up one group, and the other group consists of the remaining four variables. These two groups are outlined on the scatterplot matrix shown in **Figure 9.4**.

You can scan these plots looking for outliers (points that fall outside the bivariate ellipses) of a two–dimensional nature and identify them with square markers using the **Markers** submenu from the **Rows** menu. Now, you have identified both one– and two–dimensional outliers.

Three–Dimensional Views

To see points in three dimensions, use the **Spinning Plot** command from the **Graph** menu to launch a three–dimensional spinning platform. You can add all six variables to the spin list and then drag the **X**, **Y**, and **Z** axis tags to any combination of three variables. Your goal is to look for points away from the point cloud for each combination of three variables. You can rotate and examine each three–dimensional plot with either the spin controls or the grabber (hand) tool from the **Tools** menu.

Two outlying points appear in the view of cc14 (**x**) by hex (**y**) by chc13 (**z**) shown in **Figure 9.5**. Shift–clicking these points causes their labels, "Sulfathiazole" and "Hydroquinone," to show on the plot.

Figure 9.5 Spotting Outliers in One Three–dimensional View

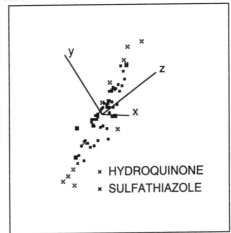

Principal Components and Biplots

Because many of the variables in the SOLUBILITY table are highly correlated, there is not as much scatter in six dimensions as you might expect. The scatter is oriented in some directions but is flattened in other directions.

To illustrate this, launch the spin platform again and add only the two highly correlated variables, eth and oct, as spin components. Select **Principal Components** from the check (✓) pop–up menu at the lower left of the platform window. The results are shown in **Figure 9.6**. Note that because the data are highly correlated, the scatter in the points runs in a narrow ellipse whose principal axis is oriented in the direction marked P1.

Figure 9.6 Two Correlated Variables with Principal Components

Components

X	eth
Y	oct
Z	Prin Comp 1
	Prin Comp 2

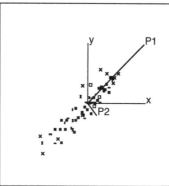 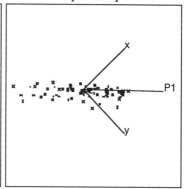

To see the greatest variation of the data in one dimension, rotate the axis so that the first principal component, P1, is horizontal. The technique of extracting these orientations that capture the highest variance is called *principal components analysis.* Principal components capture the most variation possible in the smallest number of dimensions.

If you use the **Principal Components** command in the six–variable spin platform you see the Principal Components table in **Figure 9.7**. The cumulative percent row (CumPercent) shows that the first three principal components account for 97.8% of the six–dimensional variation.

Figure 9.7 Principal Components Text Report

Principal Components

EigenValue:	4.7850	0.9408	0.1427	0.0630	0.0464	0.0221
Percent:	79.7503	15.6804	2.3779	1.0495	0.7738	0.3680
CumPercent:	79.7503	95.4307	97.8087	98.8582	99.6320	100.0000
Eigenvectors:						
eth	0.34887	0.64095	0.17653	0.63780	-0.12841	0.11419
oct	0.37314	0.56277	-0.17684	-0.67519	0.23816	0.01361
ccl4	0.43187	-0.29274	0.17821	-0.20373	-0.46785	0.66003
c6c6	0.44552	-0.14827	-0.21629	-0.01927	-0.52424	-0.67642
hex	0.42231	-0.27033	0.68072	-0.00820	0.47344	-0.24696
chcl3	0.41919	-0.30285	-0.62900	0.30884	0.45709	0.18056

On the spinning plot, principal components appear as additional *rays* labeled P1, P2, and so on as shown in **Figure 9.8**. These rays are the projections of the six–dimensional direction of the principal component in the three dimensions shown. P1 tends to be the longest ray because it shows the direction of greatest variance. P2 appears as the second longest ray and describes the next most prominent direction. The other rays become shorter and shorter.

Figure 9.8 Principal Component Rays in Three of the Variables

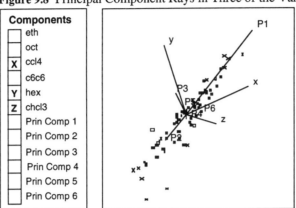

A spinning plot of the first three principal components produces the best three–dimensional representation of the six–dimensional space. In this space you can see that "Caffeine" appears as an outlier (see **Figure 9.9**). In the principal component space the variables show as rays. A plot showing both variable rays and points in an approximation of a high–dimensional space is called a *biplot* (Gabriel 1971). The configuration of the variable rays in **Figure 9.9** shows how the variables relate. Note that eth and oct seem to dominate one direction, while the other four variables cluster to define the other directions. As more dimensions (variables) are condensed into principal components, the angles between variables become indicators of their correlation. If you do a factor analysis, these directions are further refined, mapping the variables into clusters called factors.

Figure 9.9 A Biplot of Both Variables and Observations

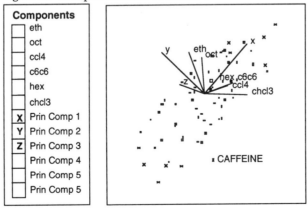

If you are looking for outliers, it is often revealing to examine the space of the last three principal components instead of the first three. The last principal components define the least popular directions of the scatter (directions with the least variation). If a point is unusual in a multivariate sense, then its prominence in the least popular direction suggests it is an outlier. Using this strategy, **Figure 9.10** shows "Sulfathiazole" as the most unusual value. The other points are in a tight cluster near the center.

Figure 9.10 Outlier in the Last Principal Components

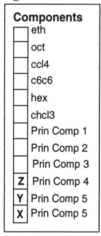
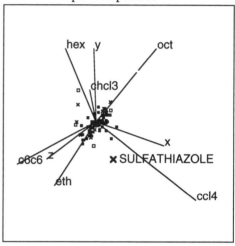

Another strategy is to plot each variable with the first two principal components and then with the last two.

In **Figure 9.11**, you see hex on the z axis and the first principal components plotted on the x and y axes.

Figure 9.11 Hex and First Two Principal Components

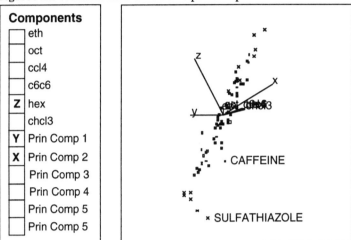

Figure 9.12 shows the variable cc14 plotted with the last two principal components.

Figure 9.12 cc14 and Last Two Principal Components

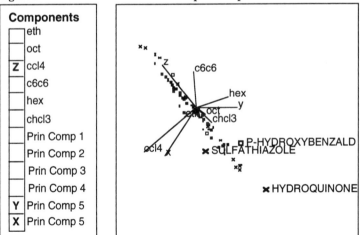

Using Colors, Markers, and the Brush Tool

Though a given plot shows two or three dimensions geometrically, you can add aspects of other dimensions by plotting the points with different markers and colors. In addition, you can use the brush tool from the **Tools** menu to see where points in areas of one plot show up on other plots.

Multivariate Distance

The basic concept of distance in several dimensions relates to the correlation of the variables. For example, in the **Correlation of Y's** scatterplot cell for c6c6 by chc13 (**Figure 9.13**), you see the compound hydroquinone located away from the point cloud. This compound is not particularly unusual in either the X or Y direction alone, but it is a two–dimensional outlier because of its unusual distance from the strong linear relationship between the two variables. The ellipse is a 95% density contour for a bivariate normal distribution with the means, standard deviations, and correlation estimated from the data. The concept of distance that takes into account the multivariate normal density contours is called *Mahalanobis distance*.

Figure 9.13 Scatterplot of Variables c6c6 and chc13

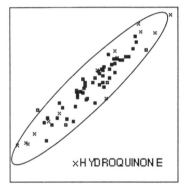

Though you can visualize only three dimensions, you can calculate the Mahalanobis distance for any number of dimensions. The six–dimensional Mahalanobis distance for the SOLUBILITY data is part of the report for the Correlation of Y's platform. The outlier distance plot in **Figure 9.14** shows the Mahalanobis distance by the row number for each point. You can click or brush points that appear as outliers in six dimensions to highlight them. In **Figure 9.14**, the five points with the greatest Mahalanobis distances are highlighted and labeled on the plot.

Figure 9.14 Mahalanobis Distance Plot to See Multivariate Outliers

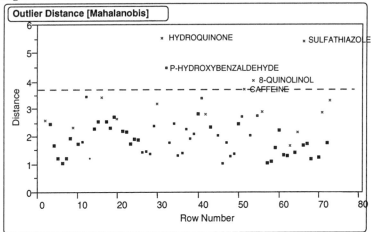

Chapter Summary

In this example, commands from the **Analyze** and **Graph** menus were used for data exploration to locate and identify unusual points. The data were first examined in one dimension using the **Distribution of Y** command and then in two dimensions using the **Correlation of Y's** command to look for unusual points in histograms and scatterplots.

Next, the **Spinning Plot** command in the **Graph** menu was used to plot three columns at a time. The technique of principal components was used to summarize six dimensions and to plot principal component rays. The Principal Components table showed that the first three principal components accounted for more than 97% of the total variation. To locate multivariate outliers, each column was plotted with the first two principal components and then with the last two principal components.

Finally, the Correlation of Y's platform produced the Mahalanobis outlier distance plot to summarize the points in six–dimensions. The multivariate outliers were highlighted and labeled in this multi-dimensional space.

See Chapter 15, "Correlations and Multivariate Techniques," in the JMP Statistics and Graphics Guide for documentation and examples of the **Correlation of Y's** command. Chapter 20, "Three–Dimensional Viewing," documents the **Spinning Plot** command.

Chapter 10
Multiple Regression
Advanced Example

Multiple regression is the technique of fitting or predicting a response by a linear combination of several regressor variables. The fitting principle is like simple linear regression, but the space of the fit is in three or more dimensions, making it more difficult to visualize. With multiple regressors, there are more opportunities to model the data well, but the process is more complicated.

This chapter begins with an example of a two–regressor fit that includes three dimensional graphics for visualization. The example is then extended to include six regressors (but unfortunately no seven–dimensional graphics to go with it).

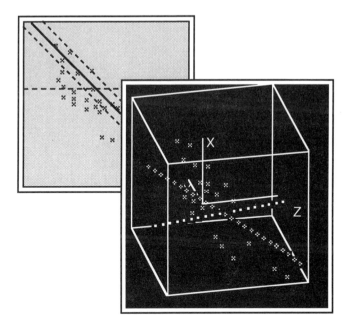

Aerobic Fitness Data

Aerobic fitness can be evaluated using a special test that measures the oxygen uptake of a person while running on a treadmill for a prescribed distance. However, it would be more economical to evaluate fitness with a formula that predicts oxygen uptake with simpler measurements.

To identify such an equation, runtime and fitness measurements were taken for 31 participants who ran 1.5 miles. The participants' ages were also recorded. The data, shown in **Figure 10.1,** are in the JMP file called FITNESS in the SAMPLE DATA folder on the Macintosh, or fitness.jmp in the data folder under Windows. For purposes of illustration, certain values of MaxPulse and RunPulse have been changed from data reported by Rawlings (1988, p.105).

Figure 10.1 The Oxygen Uptake Data Table

9 Cols / 31 Rows	Age	Weight	Oxy	Runtime	RunPulse	RstPulse	MaxPulse
1	45	87.66	37.39	14.03	186	56	192
2	54	91.63	39.20	12.88	168	44	172
3	57	73.37	39.41	12.63	174	58	176
4	44	81.42	39.44	13.08	174	63	176
5	51	69.63	40.84	10.95	168	57	172

Suppose you want to investigate age and runtime as predictors of oxygen uptake. The first step is to select the **Fit Model** command from the **Analyze** menu. This displays the Fit Model dialog in **Figure 10.2.** To specify a multiple regression model with two effects, select the Oxy column as a response variable (Y role), and both Age and Runtime as **Effects in Model** (X role).

Figure 10.2 Fit Model Dialog for Multiple Regression

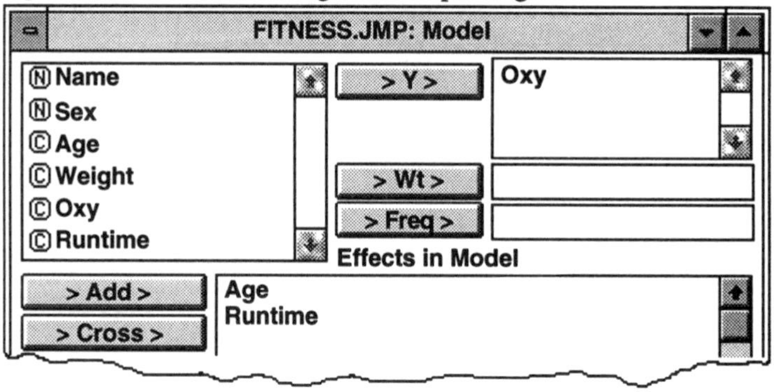

Click **Run Model** to launch the Fit Model platform. This displays the tables shown in **Figure 10.3**. These statistical reports are appropriate for a response variable and factor variables that have continuous values.

Figure 10.3 Statistical Text Reports for Fit Model Platform

Response: Oxy

Summary of Fit

RSquare	0.764769
RSquare Adj	0.747967
Root Mean Square Error	2.674424
Mean of Response	47.37581
Observations (or Sum Wgts)	31

Parameter Estimates

Effect Test

Source	Nparm	DF	Sum of Squares	F Ratio	Prob>F
Age	1	1	18.21015	2.5460	0.1218
Runtime	1	1	568.36071	79.4627	0.0000

The save ($) pop–up menu to the left of the horizontal scroll bar displays a list of save commands. You can save predicted values and the prediction equation for this model with the **Save Prediction Formula** command. This command creates a new column in the FITNESS data table called Pred Formula Oxy. Its values are the calculated predicted values for the model. To see the column's formula,

- select the Pred Formula Oxy column
- choose **Column Info** from the **Cols** menu
- click the formula display box in the lower right of the Column Info dialog.

The calculator window opens and displays the formula,

$$88.4356809 + -0.1509571 \bullet Age + -3.1987736 \bullet Runtime$$

This formula defines a plane of fit for Oxy as a function of Age and Runtime.

Note➥ For use later in this example,
- select all rows and assign them the **x** marker.
- Create a new column called Markers, and select **Row State** as its data type.
- Save the active row state assignment in the Markers column using the **Copy from RowState** pop–up command at the top of the Markers column.

Fitting Planes

JMP can show you relationships between Oxy, Runtime, and Age in three dimensions with the **Spinning Plot** command in the **Graph** menu. The plot shown in **Figure 10.4** has the **White Background** and the **Box** options in effect. These and other options are listed in the pop–up menu found on the spin control panel.

Figure 10.4 Three–Dimensional Plot of Oxy, Age, and Runtime

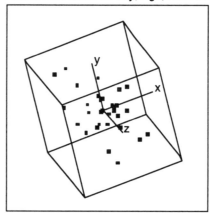

Components	
X	Age
Y	Oxy
Z	Runtime

You can also impose a fitting plane represented by a grid of values that satisfies the prediction formula for Oxy. To do this, you need to

- create a new table having a grid of Age and Runtime values for the x and y axes, and their predicted Oxy scores for the z axis.
- concatenate this grid table to the FITNESS data table.
- use the **Spinning Plot** command as before (**Figure 10.4**).

The following sections describe how to do this.

Compute a Grid for Plotting

Begin by using the **New** command in the **File** menu and create three numeric continuous columns called Age, Runtime, and Oxy to match the corresponding columns in the FITNESS table.

For convenience, select the **Set Window Name** command in the **Window** menu, and assign the name GRID to the new table.

You can use the calculator count function in the numeric functions list to compute grid values as follows:

Age Grid Open the Column Info dialog for Age, and select **Formula** as its data source. When you click **OK** and the calculator appears, select the count function from the numeric function list. It is reasonable to choose grid values for Age that range from 30 to 60. Therefore, supply the from, to, and steps arguments as shown here:

$$\text{count}\left(\text{from } 30, \text{ to } 60, \text{ in } \sqrt{n} \text{ steps}, 1 \text{ time}\right)$$

The n argument is from the Terms function list and always has the number of rows in the data table as its value during processing.

See Chapter 6, "Using the Calculator," in the *JMP User's Guide* for information about modifying formulas in the calculator window.

Runtime Grid Give the Runtime column a formula to compute values that range from 8 to 14. Therefore supply the from, to, and steps arguments as

$$\text{count}\left(\text{from } 8, \text{ to } 14, \text{ in } \sqrt{n} \text{ steps}, \sqrt{n} \text{ times}\right)$$

Oxy Values Copy the Pred Formula Oxy formula from the FITNESS table and paste it into the Oxy column calculator of the GRID table:

$$88.4356809 + -0.1509571 \cdot Age + -3.1987736 \cdot Runtime$$

Add Rows The last step is to add the number of rows, n, which determines the size of the grid. For this example use the **Add Rows** command in the **Rows** menu to add 49 rows giving a 7–by–7 grid. The table automatically fills with values.

Assign Markers Create a row state column named Markers to identify the grid points on plots. Next, select all rows and choose the diamond marker. Then use **Copy from RowState** in the pop–up menu at the top of the Markers column to copy the rowstate information into the row state column. Be sure the row state assignment is different from the one you used in the FITNESS data table.

See Chapter 6, "Using the Calculator," in the *JMP User's Guide* for information about modifying formulas in the calculator window.

You can use the **Spinning Plot** command now to see the fitted plane without the observed Markers points.

Combine the Data Tables

The FITNESS and GRID tables must be combined to plot the predicted Oxy values for the Age by Runtime grid and the observed Oxy values. You can do this easily with the **Concatenate** command in the **Tables** Menu. Click the FITNESS table to make it active, and then select the

Concatenate command. Complete its dialog by selecting GRID from the list of open tables. When you click **Concat**, the FITNESS and GRID tables append end to end and form a new untitled table.

Use the **Set Window Name** command in the **Window** menu, and call the new table **FITPLANE.JMP** (Windows) or **Fitting Planes** (Macintosh). **Figure 10.5** shows a partial listing of the new table. The first 31 rows have the observed Oxy values. Rows 32 to 80 have predicted Oxy values. Variables that were not in the GRID table have missing values.

Figure 10.5 Partial Listing of the Table with Computed Grid Values

9 Cols / 80 Rows	Age	Weight	Oxy	Runtime	RstPulse
x	29	50	70.87	55	9	48
x	30	42	68.15	60	8	40
x	31	38	81.87	60	9	48
.	32	30	.	58	8	.
.	33	35	.	58	8	.
.	34	40	.	57	8	.
.	35	45	.	56	8	.

To use the row state information, select the **Copy to RowState** pop–up command at the top of the Markers column. Then select the **Spinning Plot** command from the **Graph** menu to launch a spin plot of Age, Runtime, observed Oxy values, and the fitted plane of predicted values. The result is a graphic dramatization of the actual points marked as x's, and the plane of fit marked as dots. You can spin the plot to see how the observed points scatter about the plane.

Figure 10.6 Observed Points with the Predicted Plane of Fit

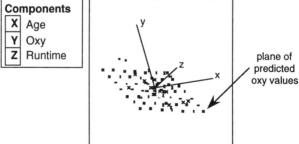

When the axes are in the home position, as shown to the left in **Figure 10.7**, you see a plot of Oxy by Age. By rotating the plot about the

y–axis to the position shown on the right, you see a plot of Oxy by Runtime, which illustrates a stronger relationship.

Figure 10.7 Rotate to See Relationships

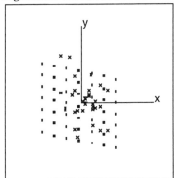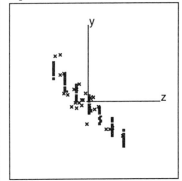

Fit Planes to Test Effects

The example in the previous section showed a plane fit to the whole model. You can also use JMP to look at hypothesis tests for each regressor and to test whether the regressor's parameter is significantly different from zero.

One way to view this test is to evaluate the difference between the current fit and the fit that occurs if you remove the regressor variable from the model. For example, consider removing the Runtime variable from the model. Then fit just the subset model, Oxy to Age, and save the prediction formula as before. The new predicted column is calculated using the formula,

$$62.4229492 +-0.3156031 \cdot Age$$

To compare this fitted line with the plane in the previous example, create a second table of grid points using this new prediction formula and concatenate it to the Fitting Planes table. Observations 81 to 129 are the new grid, which has an Age slope but is flat along Runtime.

Now you can spin the two regressor grid variables, shown on the x and z axes, and the response grid, shown on the y axis. As before, xs (x markers) mark the actual data (observed values). Diamonds show the bivariate regression plane. The dots mark the regression plane for model using the Age variable alone. Both grids represent least squares regression planes, but the dots plane has a slope of zero in the orientation of the Runtime axis. **Figure 10.8** shows the spinning plot from an angle with the **Box** display option in effect.

Figure 10.8 Three–Dimensional Plot with Regression Planes

Components	
X	Age
Y	Oxy
Z	Runtime

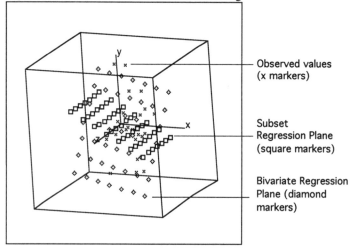

Observed values
(x markers)

Subset
Regression Plane
(square markers)

Bivariate Regression
Plane (diamond
markers)

If you look at the plot in home position for Age by Oxy as shown to the left in **Figure 10.9**, you see this subset regression showing as a line instead of a plane. The view is *edge–on* for Runtime, which eliminates it from the visual model. If you rotate the plot toward the edge–on view of Age, you see the diamond grid reduced as shown to the right in **Figure 10.9**. This view would show a straight–line fit of the x–marked points for a regression using Runtime as the only regressor.

Figure 10.9 Comparison of Three–Dimensional Views

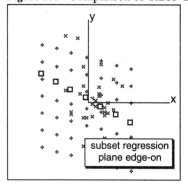

subset regression
plane edge-on

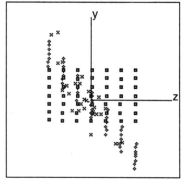

The view in **Figure 10.10** shows the bivariate regression plane edge–on, and represents the linear combination of the effects fit by the plane.

Figure 10.10 Rotating to See Relationships

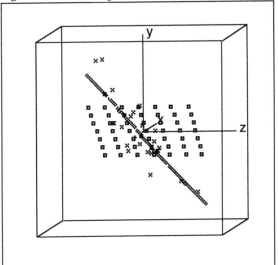

Leverage Plots: The Hypothesis–Eyed View

Suppose that you tilt the view from the previous example so that both the bivariate and subset regression planes show edge–on. **Figure 10.10** shows the subset regression plane oriented in the x direction. This view best dramatizes the difference between the fit of the bivariate regression and the subset regression. You can see how much better the fit is for the diamond–marked bivariate regression plane than for the dot–marked plane that represents the Age variable only.

Now suppose you alter this view slightly so that the Y axis is vertical but the dot–marked plane is still the horizontal edge. This view of the regression and the data is so revealing that it has a special name and a place in the text report. It is called a *leverage plot* and is an hypothesis–eyed view of the data. If you adjust the three–dimensional plot for the direction of the response as shown on the left in **Figure 10.11**, you see the leverage plot configuration for Runtime as shown on the right.

Figure 10.11 Compare Regression Planes and Leverage Plots

Components

X	Age
Y	Oxy
Z	Runtime

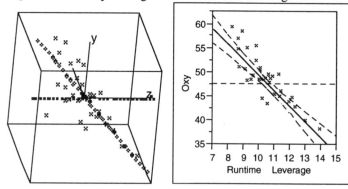

A leverage plot is important because

- the distance from each point to the line of fit represents the residual for the full model
- the distance from each point to the horizontal line represents the residual for a model constrained by the hypothesis.

The example shown in **Figure 10.11** illustrates the hypothesis that the parameter for Runtime is zero.

You can form a leverage plot for any linear hypothesis. **Figure 10.12** shows the leverage plot for testing whether **Age** is significant. Note that Age does not relate as strongly to the response as Runtime. The 95% confidence curves fully contain the horizontal line in the leverage plot for **Age**, showing that the line of fit is not significantly different from the horizontal line representing the simple mean model.

Figure 10.12 Leverage Plot for the Age Variable

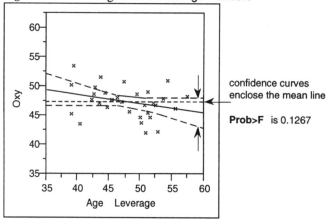

Whole Model Tests

The leverage plot in **Figure 10.13** shows the joint test of both the Age and Runtime effects in the model. This plot compares the full model with the model containing the intercept that fits the overall response mean only. This leverage plot is formed by plotting the actual observed values on the Y axis and the values predicted by the whole model on the X axis. The residual for the subset model is the distance from a point to the horizontal line drawn at the sample mean.

Figure 10.13 Leverage Plot for the Whole Model (Age and Runtime)

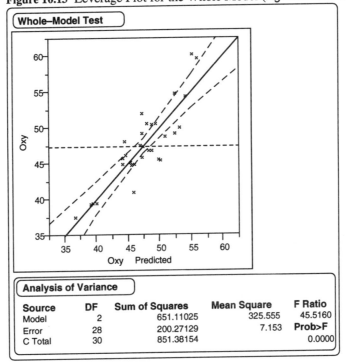

Analysis of Variance

Source	DF	Sum of Squares	Mean Square	F Ratio
Model	2	651.11025	325.555	45.5160
Error	28	200.27129	7.153	**Prob>F**
C Total	30	851.38154		0.0000

More and More Regressors

It's easy to visualize two regressors predicting a response by using fitting planes. But how can this be done with more regressors when the analysis requires more than three dimensions? In actuality, the fitting, testing, and leverage plot analyses still work for more regressors.

Continuing with the previous example, you can add Weight, RunPulse, and MaxPulse to the regression to obtain the prediction formula

$$Oxy = 102.2 - .2196\ \text{Age} - .0723\ \text{Weight} - 2.68\ \text{Runtime} - .3734\ \text{RunPulse} + .3049\ \text{MaxPulse}$$

You can look at the significance of each regressor with t ratios in the Parameter Estimates table or F ratios in the Effects Tests table (see **Figure 10.14**). Because each effect has only one parameter, the F ratios are the squares of the t ratios, and have the same significance probabilities.

The Age variable seems significant, but Weight does not. The Runtime variable seems highly significant. Both RunPulse and MaxPulse also seem significant, but MaxPulse is less significant than RunPulse.

Figure 10.14 Statistical Tables for Multiple Regression

Summary of Fit

RSquare	0.846848
RSquare Adj	0.816217
Root Mean Square Error	2.283779
Mean of Response	47.37581
Observations (or Sum Wgts)	3˙

Parameter Estimates

Term	Estimate	Std Error	t Ratio	Prob>ltl
Intercept	101.34768	11.8666	8.54	0.0000
Age	-0.212322	0.09439	-2.25	0.0335
Weight	-0.073205	0.05361	-1.37	0.1843
Runtime	-2.688436	0.34207	-7.86	0.0000
RunPulse	-0.370263	0.11772	-3.15	0.0042
MaxPulse	0.3055336	0.13454	2.27	0.0320

Effect Test

Source	Nparm	DF	Sum of Squares	F Ratio	Prob>F
Age	1	1	26.39162	5.0601	0.0335
Weight	1	1	9.72475	1.8645	0.1843
Runtime	1	1	322.16433	61.7688	0.0000
RunPulse	1	1	51.59471	9.8923	0.0042
MaxPulse	1	1	26.89778	5.1571	0.0320

Analysis of Variance

Source	DF	Sum of Squares	Mean Square	F Ratio
Model	5	720.99043	144.198	27.6472
Error	25	130.39112	5.216	Prob>F
C Total	30	851.38154		0.0000

Interpreting Leverage Plots

The leverage plots for this multiple regression model let you visualize the contribution of each effect. First, look at the whole–model leverage plot of observed versus predicted values, which illustrates the test for the whole set of regressors. The Analysis of Variance table shown in **Figure 10.15** shows a highly significant F corresponding to this plot. The confidence curves show the strong relationship because they cross the horizontal line.

Figure 10.15 Whole–Model Leverage Plot

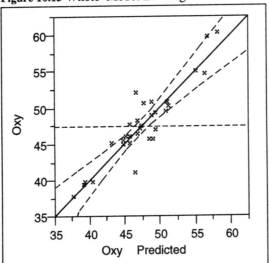

Now you can examine the leverage plots for the regressors. Each plot illustrates the residuals as they are and as they would be if that regressor were removed from the model.

The confidence curves in the leverage plot for Age, shown on the left in **Figure 10.16**, show that Age is borderline significant because the curves barely cross the horizontal line of the mean. Note that the significance of the Age effect is .03 in the text reports (**Figure 10.14**), which is only slightly different from the .05 confidence curves drawn by JMP.

The leverage plot for Weight shows that the effect is not significant. The confidence curves do not cross the horizontal line of the mean.

Figure 10.16 Leverage Plots for the Age and Weight Effects

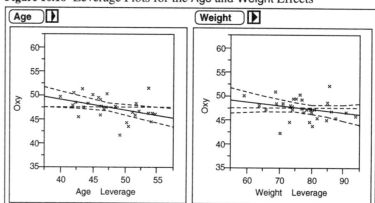

The leverage plot for Runtime (see **Figure 10.17**) shows that Runtime is the most significant of all the regressors. The Runtime leverage line and its confidence curves cross the horizontal mean at a steep angle.

Figure 10.17 Leverage Plot for the Runtime Effect

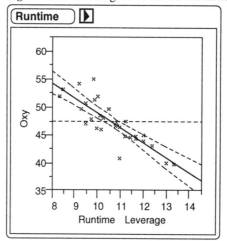

The leverage plots for RunPulse and MaxPulse are similar. Each is somewhat shrunken on the X axis. This indicates that other variables are related in a strong, linear fashion to these two regressors, which means the two effects are strongly correlated with each other.

Figure 10.18 Leverage Plots for the RunPulse and MaxPulse Effects

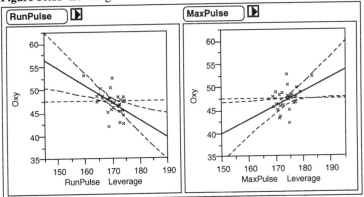

Collinearity

When two or more regressors have a strong correlation, they are said to be collinear. These regression points occupy a narrow band showing their linear relationship.

When you fit a plane representing collinear regressors, the plane fits the points well in the direction where they are widely scattered. However, in the direction where the scatter is very narrow, the fit is weak and the plane is unstable.

In text reports, this phenomenon translates into high standard errors for the parameter estimates and potentially high values for the parameter estimates themselves. This occurs because a small random error in the narrow direction can have a huge effect on the slope of the corresponding fitting plane. You can see an indication of collinearity in leverage plots when the points tend to collapse toward the center of the plot in the X direction.

The fitness example shows collinearity geometrically in the strongly correlated regressors, RunPulse and MaxPulse. To examine these regressors, you can repeat the steps that produced the Age and Runtime grids shown in **Figure 10.8**. Modify them so that one grid represents the fit of Oxy to both RunPulse and MaxPulse. The other grid is for the subset model that excludes RunPulse and shows its leverage. **Figure 10.19** shows rotated views of the regression planes. If you spin the plot, you notice that most of the points are near the intersection of the two planes. If you turn the plot so that both planes are edge–on, as shown on the right of **Figure 10.19**, then you see a view that hides most of the scatter. From that angle you can see that the fitting plane representing both variables holds no better than the subset plane. The angle of the fitting plane is steep, but the hold is unstable.

Geometrically, collinearity between two regressors means that the points they represent do not spread out in X space enough to provide stable support for a plane. Instead, the points cluster around the center causing the plane to be unstable. The regressors act as substitutes for each other to define one direction redundantly. You can cure this by dropping one of the collinear regressors from the model. You can drop either MaxPulse or RunPulse from the model because both measure essentially the same thing.

Figure 10.19 Comparison of RunPulse and MaxPulse Effects

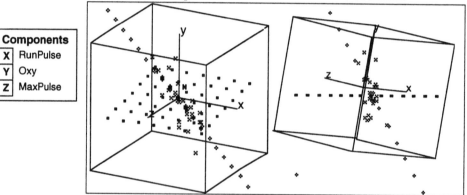

Components

X	RunPulse
Y	Oxy
Z	MaxPulse

Chapter Summary

Multiple regression uses the same fitting principle as simple regression, but accounting for significance is more subtle. Each regressor opens a new dimension for fitting a hyperplane, and its significance is tested by how much the fit suffers in its absence. Graphically, leverage plots provide the best view of each effect's partial contribution. When regressors correlate to each other, they are said to be collinear, and they define directions where the fitting hyperplane is not well supported.

References

Becker, R.A., and Cleveland, W.S. (1987), "Brushing Scatterplots," *Technometrics*, 29, 2.

Belsley, D.A., Kuh, E., and Welsch, R.E. (1980), *Regression Diagnostics*, New York: John Wiley & Sons.

Box, G.E.P., Hunter,W.G., and Hunter, J.S. (1978), *Statistics for Experimenters*, New York: John Wiley & Sons, Inc.

Daniel C. and Wood, F. (1980), *Fitting Equations to Data*, Revised Edition, New York: John Wiley & Sons, Inc.

Draper, N. and Smith, H. (1981), *Applied Regression Analysis*, 2nd Edition, New York: John Wiley & Sons, Inc.

Eppright, E.S., Fox, H.M., Fryer, B.A., Lamkin, G.H., Vivian, V.M., and Fuller, E.S. (1972), "Nutrition of infants and preschool children in the north central region of the United States of America," *World Review of Nutrition and Dietetics*, 14.

Eubank, R. L., (1988), *Spline Smoothing and Nonparametric Regression*, New York: Marcel Dekker.

Gabriel, K.R. (1982), "Biplot," *Encyclopedia of Statistical Sciences*, Volume 1, Kotz and Johnson editors, New York: John Wiley & Sons, Inc.

Hartigan J.A. and B. Kleiner (1981), "Mosaics for contingency tables," *Proceedings of the 13th Symposium on the Interface between Computer Science and Statistics*, W. F. Eddy editor, New York: Spinger.

Hawkins, D.M., (1974), "The Detection of Errors in Multivariate Data Using Koehler, Grigorus, Dunn (1988), "The Relatiohnship Between Chemical Structure and the Logarithm of the Partition," *QSAR*, 7.

Leven, J. R., Serlin, R. C., and Webne–Behrman, L. (1989), "Analysis of Variance Through Simple Correlation," *American Statistician*, 43.

Mosteller, F. and Tukey, J.W. (1977), *Data Analysis and Regression*, Reading Mass: Addison–Wesley.

Rawlings, J. O. (1988), *Applied Regression Analysis: A Research Tool*, Pacific Grove CA: Wadsworth & Books/Cole.

Sall, J. P. (1990), "Leverage Plots for General Linear Hypotheses," *American Statistician*, 308–315.

SAS Institute (1987), *SAS/Stat Guide for Personal Computers, Version 6 Edition*, Cary NC: SAS Institute Inc.

Snedecor, G.W. and Cochran, W.G. (1967), *Statistical Methods*, Ames Iowa: Iowa State University Press.

Winer, B.J. (1971), *Statistical Principals in Experimental Design*, 2nd Edition, New York: McGraw–Hill, Inc.

Index

SAS Institute Services

When you need Help...

If you are a registered user, technical support is as near as your telephone. To register, send in the registration card enclosed with the JMP product. As a registered JMP User, SAS Institute provides you with unlimited Technical Support for one year.

The Technical Support department is staffed by a group of product experts committed to providing you with knowledgeable and timely support. Technical support is available by phone (919-677-8008), fax (919-677-8123) AppleLink (SAS.TECH), or mail, Monday through Friday, 9 AM to 5 PM Eastern Time.

When you want to learn more...

Look into instructor–based training of JMP software offered by SAS Institute Inc. Seeing your data values can help you understand them better and make discoveries you might miss looking only at numbers. Two courses on JMP software are available:

- **Interactive Data Analysis Using JMP Software**

This two–day course is for scientists, researchers, engineers, quality technicians, instructors, and others who want to analyze data using JMP. In this course you learn how to analyze a variety of data using interactive methods. The statistical visualization capabilities of JMP unite classical statistical methods with new techniques in exploratory data analysis and statistical graphics.

Before selecting this course, you should have completed an undergraduate statistics course, be familiar with basic descriptive statistics, and techniques such as simple linear regression and one–way analysis of variance. You should d also know how to use a mouse to select, click, shift–click, drag, and how to select commands from menus.

- **Design and Analysis of Experiments Using JMP Software**

This one–day course is for quality technicians especially in manufacturing. It is valuable for scientists and researchers responsible for designing experiments, conducting them, and analyzing results.

Before selecting this course, you should have completed Interactive Data Analysis Using JMP software or have equivalent knowledge and experience. You should also have completed a graduate–level course in experimental design or have equivalent knowledge and experience.

When and Where

The JMP courses are taught as back–to–back in SAS regional training centers, and can also be taught at your location. To register for a public course, call a course registrar in Cary, NC at 919-677-8000, extension 5005, or call the Institute training center nearest you. For more information about the content of the courses, call 919-677-8000, extension 7205. To schedule a course at your location, call an Education Account Representative, at extension 7321.